Shakespeare

THE ANIMATED TALES

Shakespeare The Animated Tales is a multinational venture conceived by S4C,
Channel 4 Wales. Produced in Russia, Wales and England, the series has been financed by S4C
and the BBC (UK), Christmas Films (Russia), Home Box Office (USA) and Fujisankei (Japan).

Academic Panel
Professor Stanley Wells
Dr Rex Gibson

Educational Adviser
Michael Marland

Publishing Editor and Co-ordinator
Jane Fior

Book Design
Fiona Macmillan and Ness Wood

Animation Director for *Julius Caesar*
Yuri Kulakov of Christmas Films, Moscow

Animation Director for *As You Like It*
Alexei Karaiev of Christmas Films, Moscow

Animation Director for *Richard III*
Natalia Orlova of Christmas Films, Moscow

Animation Director for *The Taming of the Shrew*
Aida Ziablikova of Christmas Films, Moscow

Animation Director for *Othello*
Nikolai Serebriakov of Christmas Films, Moscow

Animation Director for *The Winter's Tale*
Stanislav Sokolov of Christmas Films, Moscow

Series Editors
Martin Lamb and Penelope Middelboe, Right Angle, Tenby, Wales

Executive Producers
Christopher Grace (S4C)
Elizabeth Babakhina (Christmas Films)

Associate Producer
Theresa Plummer Andrews (BBC)

First published in 1994
by William Heinemann Ltd
an imprint of Reed Consumer Books Ltd
Michelin House, 81 Fulham Road, London SW3 6RB
and Auckland, Melbourne, Singapore and Toronto
Copyright © Shakespeare Animated Films/Christmas Films 1994

ISBN 0 434 96784 X

A CIP catalogue record for this title is available
from the British Library

Printed in Great Britain by BPC Paulton Books Limited

The publishers would like to thank Paul Cox
for the series logo illustration,
Carol Kemp for her calligraphy,
Theo Crosby for the use of his painting of the Globe,
and Rosa Fior and Celia Salisbury Jones
for their help on the books.

Shakespeare
THE ANIMATED TALES

ABRIDGED BY
LEON GARFIELD

JULIUS CAESAR

AS YOU LIKE IT

RICHARD III

*THE TAMING
OF THE SHREW*

OTHELLO

THE WINTER'S TALE

HEINEMANN · LONDON

CONTENTS

William Shakespeare

Martin Droeshout sculpsit London

WILLIAM SHAKESPEARE

NEXT TO GOD, A wise man once said, Shakespeare created most. In the thirty-seven plays that are his chief legacy to the world – and surely no-one ever left a richer! – human nature is displayed in all its astonishing variety.

He has enriched the stage with matchless comedies, tragedies, histories, and, towards the end of his life, with plays that defy all description, strange plays that haunt the imagination like visions.

His range is enormous: kings and queens, priests, princes and merchants, soldiers, clowns and drunkards, murderers, pimps, whores, fairies, monsters and pale, avenging ghosts 'strut and fret their hour upon the stage'. Murders and suicides abound; swords flash, blood flows, poison drips, and lovers sigh; yet there is always time for old men to talk of growing apples and for gardeners to discuss the weather.

In the four hundred years since they were written, they have become known and loved in every land; they are no longer the property of one country and one people, they are the priceless possession of the world.

His life, from what we know of it, was not astonishing. The stories that have attached themselves to him are remarkable only for their ordinariness: poaching deer, sleeping off a drinking bout under a wayside tree. There are no duels, no loud, passionate loves, no excesses of any kind. He was not one of your unruly geniuses whose habits are more interesting than their works. From all accounts, he was of a gentle, honourable disposition, a good businessman, and a careful father.

He was born on April 23rd 1564, to John and Mary Shakespeare of Henley Street, Stratford-upon-Avon. He was their third child and first son. When he was four or five he began his education at the local petty school. He left the local grammar school when he was about fourteen, in all probability to help in his father's glove-making shop. When he was eighteen, he married Anne Hathaway, who lived in a nearby village. By the time he was twenty-one, he was the father of three children, two daughters and a son.

Then, it seems, a restless mood came upon him. Maybe he travelled, maybe he was, as some say, a schoolmaster in the country; but at some time during the next seven years, he went to London and found employment in the theatre. When he was twenty-eight, he was already well enough known as an actor and playwright to excite the spiteful envy of a rival, who referred to him as 'an upstart crow'.

He mostly lived and worked in London until his mid-forties, when he returned to his family and home in Stratford, where he remained in prosperous circumstances until his death on April 23rd 1616, his fifty-second birthday.

He left behind him a widow, two daughters (his son died in childhood), and the richest imaginary world ever created by the human mind.

LEON GARFIELD

The list of the plays contained in the First Folio of 1623. This was the first collected edition of Shakespeare's plays and was gathered together by two of his fellow actors, John Hemmings and Henry Condell.

A CATALOGVE

of the feuerall Comedies, Histories, and Tragedies contained in this Volume.

THE THEATRE IN SHAKESPEARE'S DAY

IN 1989 AN ARCHAEOLOGICAL discovery was made on the south bank of the Thames that sent shivers of delight through the theatre world. A fragment of Shakespeare's own theatre, the Globe, where many of his plays were first performed, had been found.

This discovery has fuelled further interest in how Shakespeare himself conceived and staged his plays. We know a good deal already, and archaeology as well as documentary research will no doubt reveal more, but although we can only speculate on some of the details, we have a good idea of what the Elizabethan theatre-goer saw, heard and smelt when he went to see a play by William Shakespeare at the Globe.

It was an entirely different experience from anything we know today. Modern theatres have roofs to keep out the weather. If it rained on the Globe, forty per cent of the play-goers got wet. Audiences today sit on cushioned seats, and usually (especially if the play is by Shakespeare) watch and listen in respectful silence. In the Globe, the floor of the theatre was packed with a riotous crowd of garlic-reeking apprentices, house servants and artisans, who had each paid a penny to stand for the entire duration of the play, to buy nuts and apples from the food-sellers, to refresh themselves with bottled ale, relieve themselves, perhaps, into buckets by the back wall, to talk, cheer, catcall, clap and hiss if the play did not please them.

In the galleries that rose in curved tiers around the inside of the building sat those who could afford to pay two pennies for a seat, and the benefits of a roof over their heads. Here, the middle ranking citizens, the merchants, the sea captains, the clerks from the Inns of Court, would sit crammed into their small eighteen inch space and look down upon the 'groundlings' below. In the 'Lords' room', the rich and the great, noblemen and women, courtiers and foreign ambassadors had to pay sixpence each for the relative comfort and luxury of their exclusive position directly above the stage, where they smoked tobacco, and overlooked the rest.

We are used to a stage behind an arch, with wings on either side, from which the actors come on and into which they disappear. In the Globe, the stage was a platform thrusting out into the middle of the floor, and the audience, standing in the central yard, surrounded it on three sides. There were no wings. Three doors at the back of the stage were used for all exits and entrances. These were sometimes covered by a curtain, which could be used as a prop.

Today we sit in a darkened theatre or cinema, and look at a brilliantly lit stage or screen, or we sit at home in a small, private world of our own, watching a luminous television screen. The close-packed, rowdy crowd at the Globe, where the play started at two o'clock in the afternoon, had no artificial light to enhance their illusion. It was the words that moved them. They came to listen, rather than to see.

No dimming lights announced the start of the play. A blast from a trumpet and three sharp knocks warned the audience that the action was about to begin. In the broad daylight, the actor could see the audience as clearly as the audience could see him. He spoke directly to the crowd, and held them with his eyes, following their reactions. He could play up to the raucous laughter that greeted the comical, bawdy scenes, and gauge the emotional response to the higher flights of poetry. Sometimes he even improvised speeches of his own. He was surrounded by, enfolded by, his audience.

The stage itself would seem uncompromisingly bare to our eyes. There was no scenery. No painted backdrops suggested a forest, or a castle, or the sumptuous interior of a palace. Shakespeare painted the scenery with his words, and the imagination of the audience did the rest.

Props were brought onto the stage only when they were essential for the action. A bed would be carried on when a character needed to lie on it. A throne would be let down from above when a king needed to sit on it. Torches and lanterns would suggest that it was dark, but the main burden of persuading an audience, at three o'clock in the afternoon, that it was in fact the middle of the night, fell upon the language.

In our day, costume designers create a concept as part of the production of a play into which each costume fits. Shakespeare's actors were responsible for their own costumes. They would use what was to hand in the 'tiring house' (dressing room), or supplement it out of their own pockets. Classical, medieval and Tudor clothes could easily appear side by side in the same play.

No women actors appeared on a public stage until many years after

Shakespeare's death, for at that time it would have been considered shameless. The parts of young girls were played by boys. The parts of older women were played by older men.

In 1613 the Globe theatre was set on fire by a spark from a cannon during a performance of Henry VIII, and it burnt to the ground. The actors, including Shakespeare himself, dug into their own pockets and paid for it to be rebuilt. The new theatre lasted until 1642, when it closed again. Now, in the 1990s, the Globe is set to rise again as a committed band of actors, scholars and enthusiasts are raising the money to rebuild Shakespeare's theatre in its original form a few yards from its previous site.

From the time when the first Globe theatre was built until today, Shakespeare's plays have been performed in a vast variety of languages, styles, costumes and techniques, on stage, on film, on television and in animated film. Shakespeare himself, working within the round wooden walls of his theatre, would have been astonished by it all.

PATRICK SPOTTISWOODE
Director of Education,
Globe Theatre Museum

SHAKESPEARE TODAY

SHAKESPEARE IS ALIVE TODAY! Although William Shakespeare the man lies long buried in Stratford-upon-Avon parish church, he lives on in countless millions of hearts and minds.

Imagine that cold April day in 1616. The small funeral procession labours slowly along Church Street. Huge black horses draw the wooden cart bearing the simple coffin. On the coffin, a few daffodils and primroses, plucked only minutes before from the garden of New Place, gravely nod with each jolt and jar of the rutted road.

Most of Stratford's citizens have turned out, muffled against the biting wind, to see the last appearance of their wealthy neighbour. You couldn't call it a crowd. Just small respectful groups clustering the dry places on the roadside, careful to avoid the mud splashed up by the great hooves of the lumbering horses.

Men and women briefly bow their heads as the dead man and the black-clad mourners pass. The townspeople share their opinions, as neighbours do. "He used to do some acting, didn't he?" "Made a lot of money in London. Writing plays, I think." "Used to come home once a year to see his family, but nobody here really knew a lot about Master Shakespeare." "Wasn't he a poet?" "Big landowner hereabouts anyway. All those fields over at Welcombe."

Past the Guild Chapel where he had worshipped as a boy. Past the school where long ago his imagination was fired by language. At the churchyard gate, under the sad elms, six men effortlessly heave the coffin on to their shoulders. William Shakespeare is about to enter his parish church for the last time.

Nobody at that long ago funeral guessed that they were saying goodbye to a man who would become the most famous Englishman of his age – perhaps of all time.

Shakespeare lives on. He weaves familiar themes into his tales: the conflicts between parents and children, love at first sight, the power struggles of war and politics. His language is heard everywhere. If you ever call someone 'a blinking idiot' or 'a tower of strength', or describe them as 'tongue-tied', or suffering from 'green-eyed jealousy', or being 'dead as a doornail', you are speaking the language of Shakespeare.

If you say 'it was Greek to me' or 'parting is such sweet sorrow', or that something is 'too much of a good thing' and that you 'have not slept one wink', the words of Shakespeare are alive in your mouth. Shakespeare's language has a power all of its own, rich in emotional intensity. Because he was a poet who wrote plays, he could make even the simplest words utterly memorable. All around the world people know Hamlet's line 'To be or not to be, that is the question.'

Shakespeare is still performed today because of the electrifying power of his storytelling. Whether his story is about love or murder, or kings and queens, he keeps you on the edge of your seat wanting to know what happens next.

He created well over nine hundred characters in his plays. However large or small the part, each character springs vividly to life in performance. They live in our imagination because they are so much like people today. They experience the same emotions that everyone feels and recognises: love, jealousy, fear, courage, ambition, pride … and a hundred others.

In every play, Shakespeare invites us to imagine what the characters are like, and for nearly four hundred years people have accepted Shakespeare's invitation. The plays have been re-imagined in very many ways. They have been shortened, added to, and set in very different periods of history. They have been translated into many languages and performed all over the world. Shakespeare lives because all persons in every age and every society can make their own interpretations and performances of Shakespeare.

The creators of *The Animated Tales* have re-imagined *Julius Caesar* in a 26 minute animated film. You too can make your own living Shakespeare. Read the text that follows, and watch the video. Then try reading the play either by yourself, changing your voice to suit the different characters, or with friends, and record it on a tape recorder. If you have a toy theatre, try staging it with characters and scenery that you make and paint yourself. Or collect together a cast and create your own production for your family and friends.

DR REX GIBSON

Dr Rex Gibson is the director of the Shakespeare and Schools Project which is part of the Institute of Education at the University of Cambridge.

In 1994 he was awarded the Sam Wanamaker International Shakespeare Award for his outstanding contribution to the world's knowledge of the works of Shakespeare.

WHAT THEY SAID OF HIM

One will ever find, in searching his works, new cause for astonishment and admiration.

GOETHE

Shakespeare was a writer of all others the most calculated to make his readers better as well as wiser.

SAMUEL TAYLOR COLERIDGE

An overstrained enthusiasm is more pardonable with respect to Shakespeare than the want of it; for our admiration cannot easily surpass his genius.

WILLIAM HAZLITT

It required three hundred years for England to begin to hear those two words that the whole world cries in her ear – William Shakespeare.

VICTOR HUGO

He has left nothing to be said about nothing or anything.

JOHN KEATS

The stream of time, which is continually washing the dissoluble fabrics of other poets, passes without injury by the adamant of Shakespeare.

SAMUEL JOHNSON

Julius Caesar

The Tragedy of Julius Caesar has been called the greatest play about politics ever written. It is a tale of envy, pride and bloated ambition, of treachery and murder. It is the story of four great men and their struggle for power: of Brutus, a good man, who, for what he believes to be the best of reasons, commits the worst of crimes; of Cassius, 'lean and hungry' Cassius, whose love for his friend Brutus causes him to override his own better judgement and so lead his cause to ruin; of Mark Antony, the 'masker and reveller', who is yet the cleverest and most ruthless politician of them all; and it is the story of Julius Caesar himself, a man who has come to believe so much in his own greatness that he thinks himself a god – "Wilt thou lift up Olympus?" he demands of those who kneel before him to beg for mercy for a friend; and the next instant he perishes under a raging hail of knives …

Leon Garfield

The curtain rises on a great procession through the streets of Rome. The whole city waits to cheer Julius Caesar, ruler of the world, as he returns in triumph from another glorious victory. Calphurnia, his wife, and all the great ones of Rome follow after him like faithful dogs. Suddenly, a voice cries out.

SOOTHSAYER   Caesar!

CAESAR   Speak. Caesar is turned to hear.

SOOTHSAYER   Beware the ides of March.

The soothsayer is brought before Caesar.

CAESAR   What say'st thou to me now? Speak once again.

SOOTHSAYER   Beware the ides of March.

CAESAR   (*staring at the soothsayer*) He is a dreamer. Let us leave him. Pass.

The procession passes on. Brutus and Cassius remain behind. They lean against the plinth of a huge statue of Caesar, which dwarfs them. There are images of Caesar all around.

CASSIUS   Brutus, I have not from your eyes that gentleness and show of love as I was wont to have.

BRUTUS   Poor Brutus, with himself at war, forgets the shows of love to other men. (*There is a sound of distant shouting.*) What means this shouting? I do fear the people choose Caesar for their king.

CASSIUS   Ay, do you fear it? Then must I think you would not have it so.

BRUTUS   I would not, Cassius; yet I love him well.

There is another shout.

CASSIUS   Why, man, he doth bestride the narrow world like a Colossus, and we petty men walk under his huge legs, and peep about to find ourselves dishonourable graves. What should be in that 'Caesar'? Why should that name be sounded more than yours?

BRUTUS   Caesar is returning!

Caesar enters, followed by his retinue, which includes his friend Mark Antony. He looks angry, and his followers disturbed.

CAESAR   Antonius!

ANTONY   Caesar?

CAESAR   Let me have men about me that are fat, sleek-headed men and such as sleep a-nights. Yond Cassius has a lean and hungry look, he thinks too much; such men are dangerous.

ANTONY   Fear him not, Caesar, he's not dangerous. He is a noble Roman and well given.

CAESAR   Would he were fatter! but I fear him not.

Caesar raises his arm. Trumpets sound, and the procession continues. Casca stays.

BRUTUS   Casca, tell us what hath chanced today, that Caesar looks so sad.

CASCA   Why, there was a crown offered him. He put it by; but to my thinking, he would fain have had it.

CASSIUS   Who offered him the crown?

CASCA   Mark Antony.

BRUTUS   What was the second noise for?

CASCA   Why for that too; then he put it by again, but to my thinking he was very loath to lay his fingers off it. As he refused it, the rabblement hooted, and uttered such a deal of stinking breath, that it had, almost, choked Caesar, for he fell down at it.

BRUTUS   'Tis very like; he hath the falling sickness.

CASSIUS   No, Caesar hath it not; but you, and I, and honest Casca, we have the falling sickness.

CASCA   I know not what you mean by that. Farewell, both.

He goes.

BRUTUS   Tomorrow, if you please to speak with me, come home to me, and I will wait for you.

CASSIUS   I will do so; till then, think of the world.

Brutus leaves. Cassius is left alone.

CASSIUS   Well, Brutus, thou art noble; yet I see thy honourable mettle may be wrought; for who so firm that cannot be seduced?

A wild night torn by thunder and lightning. Cassius enters, hastening along a streaming, glaring street. A shadowy figure meets him. It is Casca.

CASSIUS   Who's there?

CASCA   A Roman.

CASSIUS   Casca, by your voice.

CASCA   Cassius, what night is this! Whoever knew the heavens menace so?

CASSIUS   Those that have known the earth so full of faults.

CASCA   They say the senators tomorrow mean to establish Caesar as a king.

CASSIUS	I know where I will wear this dagger then: Cassius from bondage will deliver Cassius.
CASCA	So will I. Hold, my hand.

They clasp hands. The thunder and lightning grow more violent. Cinna enters.

CASCA	Stand close a while.
CASSIUS	'Tis Cinna. He is a friend. (*The conspirators huddle close together.*)
CINNA	O Cassius, if you could but win the noble Brutus to our party –
CASSIUS	Good Cinna, take this paper, and throw this in at his window. Three parts of him is ours already, and the man entire upon the next encounter yields him ours!

Cinna goes.

Brutus is walking in his orchard. The fury of the heavens has increased and the dark fabric of the sky is ripped apart by comets and shooting stars.

BRUTUS	It must be by his death. And for my part I know no personal cause to spurn at him for the general. He would be crowned; how that might change his nature. Crown him? – that – and then I grant we put a sting in him. Therefore think of him as a serpent's egg and kill him in the shell.

His servant Lucius enters.

LUCIUS   The taper burneth in your closet, sir. Searching the window for a flint, I found this paper. (*He gives him a scroll.*)

BRUTUS   Is not tomorrow, boy, the ides of March?

LUCIUS   (*nodding in the affirmative*) Sir, March is wasted fifteen days.

There is knocking on the gate.

BRUTUS   Go to the gate, somebody knocks.

Lucius leaves. Brutus opens the scroll and reads.

'Brutus, thou sleep'st. Awake and see thyself! Speak, strike, redress!' Between the acting of a dreadful thing and the first motion, all the interim is like a phantasma or a hideous dream.

Cassius enters, with Decius, Casca, Cinna, Metellus and Trebonius. These last are all cloaked and hooded.

CASSIUS   Good morrow, Brutus.

BRUTUS   Know I these men that come along with you?

CASSIUS   Yes, every man of them.

Cassius reveals himself.

BRUTUS   Give me your hands all over, one by one.

DECIUS   Shall no man else be touched but only Caesar?

CASSIUS   Decius, well urged. I think it is not meet Mark Antony, so well beloved of Caesar, should outlive Caesar.

BRUTUS   Our course will seem too bloody, to cut the head off and then hack the limbs. Let's be sacrificers, but not butchers, Cassius. And for Mark Antony, think not of him.

CASSIUS   Yet I fear him.

TREBONIUS Let him not die.

CASSIUS   But it is doubtful yet whether Caesar will come forth today or no, for he is superstitious grown of late.

DECIUS   Never fear that. I can o'ersway him, and I will bring him to the Capitol.

A clock strikes three.

TREBONIUS 'Tis time to part.

The conspirators leave. Brutus is left alone. Presently his wife, Portia, comes out of the house and approaches him.

PORTIA   Brutus, my lord!

BRUTUS   Wherefore rise you now?

PORTIA   Dear my lord, make me acquainted with your cause of grief.

BRUTUS   Portia, I am not well in health, and that is all.

PORTIA   No, my Brutus, you have some sick offence within your mind and, upon my knees I charm you, by all your vows of love, that you unfold to me, why you are heavy, and what men tonight have had resort to you, who hid their faces even from the darkness. (*She kneels.*)

BRUTUS   Kneel not, gentle Portia.

PORTIA   I should not need, if you were gentle Brutus. Dwell I but in the suburbs of your good pleasure? If it be no more, Portia is Brutus' harlot, not his wife.

BRUTUS   You are my true and honourable wife, and by and by thy bosom shall partake the secrets of my heart.

It is morning and another wife is filled with fears for her husband. In Caesar's house, Calphurnia pleads with him to stay at home.

CALPHURNIA   What mean you, Caesar? You shall not stir out of your house today.

CAESAR   Caesar shall forth.

CALPHURNIA   I never stood on ceremonies, yet now they fright me. There is one within recounts most horrid sights. A lioness hath whelped in the streets, and graves have yawned and yielded up their dead; fierce fiery warriors fight upon the clouds, which drizzled blood upon the Capitol.

CAESAR   These predictions are to the world in general as to Caesar.

CALPHURNIA   When beggars die, there are no comets seen; the heavens themselves blaze forth the death of princes.

CAESAR   Cowards die many times before their deaths; the valiant never taste of death but once.

CALPHURNIA   Alas, my lord, your wisdom is consumed in confidence. Call it my fear that keeps you in the house and not your own.

She kneels. Caesar smiles indulgently.

CAESAR   For thy humour, I will stay at home.

Decius enters.

DECIUS   Caesar, all hail!

CAESAR   Decius, you are come in very happy time to bear my greetings to the senators, and tell them that I will not come today.

DECIUS   Most mighty Caesar, let me know some cause.

CAESAR   The cause is in my will, I will not come: that is enough to satisfy the senate. But because I love you I will let you know. Calphurnia here, my wife, stays me at home. She dreamt tonight she saw my statue, which, like a fountain with an hundred spouts, did run pure blood, and many lusty Romans came smiling and did bathe their hands in it.

DECIUS   This dream is all amiss interpreted, it signifies that from you great Rome shall suck reviving blood.

CAESAR   And this way have you well expounded it.

DECIUS   And know it now: the senate have concluded to give this day a crown to mighty Caesar. If you shall send them word you will not come, their minds may change.

CAESAR   How foolish do your fears seem now, Calphurnia! I will go.

A great crowd awaits outside the Capitol. There are shouts of 'Caesar! Caesar!' The shouts increase in volume and excitement. The faces of the crowd are joyful, eager. Caesar sees the soothsayer and approaches him, followed by Brutus, Cassius and the other conspirators.

CAESAR   The ides of March are come.

SOOTHSAYER   Ay, Caesar, but not gone.

Caesar shrugs his shoulders, and mounts the steps into the Capitol. The conspirators follow. A senator murmurs to Cassius.

SENATOR   I wish your enterprise today may thrive.

As he slips away, there is a great amount of nervous plucking at each other's sleeves and cloaks. The conspirators mutter to one another fearfully.

CASSIUS   I fear our purpose is discovered! Brutus, what shall be done?

BRUTUS   Cassius, be constant. Popilius Lena speaks not of our purposes, for look, he smiles, and Caesar doth not change.

CINNA   Casca, you are the first that rears your hand.

The conspirators encircle Caesar. Metellus kneels, then the others. Casca moves behind. As they kneel, they plead.

METELLUS   Most high, most mighty . . .

CINNA   O Caesar!

CASSIUS   Pardon, Caesar! Caesar, pardon!

Caesar, turning from one supplicant to another, pulls his clutched gown free.

BRUTUS   I kiss thy hand, but not in flattery, Caesar.

CAESAR   What Brutus?

DECIUS   Great Caesar!

CAESAR   Hence! Wilt thou lift up Olympus?

CASCA   Speak hands for me!

He stabs Caesar in the neck. The others rush upon the staggering Caesar and slash and stab at him. He continues to resist until he sees Brutus.

CAESAR   Et tu, Brute? – (*Seeing Brutus, Caesar covers his face with a gown in pitiful surrender.*) Then fall, Caesar!

Brutus strikes. Caesar dies, and falls at the base of Pompey's statue which has been splattered with blood. There is so much blood from Caesar and the wounded conspirators that it appears to spout blood, as in Calphurnia's dream. There is a moment of terrible silence.

CINNA   Liberty! Freedom! Tyranny is dead!

CASSIUS   Liberty! Freedom!

There is sudden turmoil in the senate, as the senators fly for their lives.

BRUTUS   Fly not, stand still, ambition's debt is paid!

*But no one listens, and, presently, the conspirators are alone
with their crime.*

BRUTUS   Then walk we forth even to the market-place. Let's all cry,
              'Peace, Freedom and Liberty!'.

*As the conspirators kneel and smear their hands with blood, a
shadow falls across them.*

CASSIUS   Where is Mark Antony? (*He appears.*)

BRUTUS   Welcome, Mark Antony.

ANTONY   O mighty Caesar! dost thou lie so low? I know not, gentlemen,
              what you intend, who else must be let blood; if I myself there is
              no hour so fit as Caesar's death hour.

BRUTUS   O Antony! Beg not your death of us —

CASSIUS   Your voice shall be as strong as any man's in the disposing of
              new dignities.

BRUTUS Only be patient till we have appeased the multitude, and then we will deliver you the cause why I, that did love Caesar when I struck him, have thus proceeded.

ANTONY I doubt not of your wisdom. (*He shakes the conspirators' hands.*) And am, moreover, suitor that I may produce his body to the market-place, and in the pulpit, as becomes a friend, speak in the order of his funeral.

BRUTUS You shall, Mark Antony.

CASSIUS (*aside*) You know not what you do. Know you how much the people may be moved by that which he will utter?

BRUTUS I will myself into the pulpit first, and show the reason of our Caesar's death.

CASSIUS I know not what may fall; I like it not.

The conspirators leave. There is the roar of a crowd while Brutus speaks.

BRUTUS Romans, countrymen, and lovers, hear me for my cause.

ANTONY   (*to Caesar's body*) Are all thy conquests, glories, triumphs, spoils, shrunk to this little measure? O pardon me, thou bleeding piece of earth, that I am meek and gentle with these butchers. Woe to the hand that shed this costly blood! (*He pauses.*) Cry havoc, and let slip the dogs of war!

Outside, Brutus addresses the people.

BRUTUS   As Caesar loved me, I weep for him; as he was valiant, I honour him; but, as he was ambitious, I slew him! (*There are loud cheers.*) I have the same dagger for myself, when it shall please my country to need my death!

ALL   Live, Brutus! live, live!

1ST PLEBEIAN   Bring him with triumph home unto his house!

2ND PLEBEIAN   Give him a statue —

3RD PLEBEIAN   Let him be Caesar!

Mark Antony enters, bearing Caesar's body. He lays it down on the ground. Brutus leaves.

ANTONY   Friends, Romans, countrymen, lend me your ears! I come to bury Caesar, not to praise him. The evil that men do lives after them, the good is oft interred with their bones. So let it be with Caesar. (*During the above, the crowd begins to stir and murmur.*) He was my friend, faithful and just to me; but Brutus says he was ambitious, and Brutus is an honourable man. When that the poor have cried, Caesar hath wept; ambition should be made of sterner stuff; yet Brutus says he was ambitious, and Brutus is an honourable man. You all did see I thrice presented him a kingly crown, which he did thrice refuse. Was this ambition?

1ST PLEBEIAN   Methinks there is much reason in his sayings.

2ND PLEBEIAN   Caesar has had great wrong.

3RD PLEBEIAN   I fear there will a worse come in his place.

4TH PLEBEIAN   There's not a nobler man in Rome than Antony!

The crowd begins to surge. The cry of 'Antony! Antony! Antony!' goes up.

ANTONY	If you have tears, prepare to shed them now. Look, in this place ran Cassius' dagger through; see what a rent the envious Casca made.
1ST PLEBEIAN	O piteous spectacle!
2ND PLEBEIAN	O noble Caesar!
ANTONY	Through this the well-beloved Brutus stabbed. This was the most unkindest cut of all.
4TH PLEBEIAN	O traitors, villains!
2ND PLEBEIAN	We will be revenged!
ALL	Revenge! Seek! Burn! Fire! Kill! Let not a traitor live!

The crowd, like a river in full spate, now bursts its banks and rushes through the streets, tearing up benches, and anything that comes in its way, shouting—

ALL	Away, away! Revenge, revenge!

They seize on a poor, unfortunate man. He struggles to be free.

CINNA THE POET	I am Cinna the poet! I am Cinna the poet! I am not Cinna the conspirator!

Cinna is dragged away, screaming.

ANTONY   (*watching the riot with grim satisfaction*) Now let it work.
           Mischief, thou art afoot, take thou what course thou wilt.

*The conspirators flee from the fury of the people. Anyone
against whom there is the smallest suspicion is ruthlessly put to
death by order of Mark Antony and young Octavius, Caesar's
nephew and heir to his name. Brutus and Cassius escape into
Asia where they raise armies to march against Antony and
Octavius. But all is not well between the friends: Brutus
accuses Cassius of taking bribes.*

*Outside Brutus' tent, officers are listening, frowning and
worried. Within the tent, Brutus and Cassius confront one
another. Both are dressed for battle. Cassius looks the more
seasoned and professional.*

CASSIUS	I – an itching palm! When Caesar lived, he durst not thus have moved me.
BRUTUS	You durst not so have tempted him. (*With clenched fists*) Remember March, the ides of March remember. Did not great Julius bleed for justice' sake?
CASSIUS	Do not presume too much upon my love, I may do that I shall be sorry for.
BRUTUS	You have done that you should be sorry for.
CASSIUS	You love me not.
BRUTUS	I do not like your faults.
CASSIUS	A friendly eye could never see such faults.
BRUTUS	O Cassius, I am sick of many griefs. Portia is dead.
CASSIUS	How 'scaped I killing when I crossed you so? Upon what sickness?
BRUTUS	Impatient of my absence, and grief that young Octavius with Mark Antony have made themselves so strong; with this she fell distract and swallowed fire.

CASSIUS Portia, art thou gone?

BRUTUS No more, I pray you. I have here received letters that young Octavius and Mark Antony come down upon us with a mighty power. What think you of marching to Philippi presently?

CASSIUS I do not think it good.

BRUTUS Our cause is ripe. The enemy increaseth every day; we, at the height, are ready to decline. There is a tide in the affairs of men, which taken at the flood, leads on to fortune. And we must take the current when it serves.

CASSIUS Then with your will, go on; we'll along ourselves, and meet them at Philippi.

Cassius leaves Brutus. The page, Lucius, is fast asleep in a corner. Brutus gently covers him and seats himself at his table. The yellow flame flickers, then begins to burn blue.

The ghost of Caesar enters.

BRUTUS	Ha! Who comes here? Art thou any thing? Speak to me what thou art!
GHOST	Thy evil spirit, Brutus.
BRUTUS	Why com'st thou?
GHOST	To tell thee thou shalt see me at Philippi.
BRUTUS	Well: then I shall see thee again?
GHOST	Ay.

The ghost vanishes.

On the plain of Philippi, Octavius and Mark Antony await the coming battle. Their great army stretches behind them. In the distance there is a faint glimmer of the enemy's steel.

ANTONY   Octavius, lead your battle softly on upon the left hand of the
           even field.

OCTAVIUS   Upon the right hand, I. Keep thou the left.

ANTONY   Why do you cross me?

OCTAVIUS   I do not cross you, but I will do so.

           Octavius and Antony return to their lines.
           Cassius confers with an officer.

CASSIUS   (*very sadly to an officer*) This is my birthday; as this very day
           was Cassius born. Be thou witness that against my will am I
           compelled to set upon one battle all our liberties. (*Brutus joins
           him.*) Now, most noble Brutus, if we lose this battle, are you
           contented to be led in triumph through the streets of Rome?

BRUTUS   No, Cassius, no. But this same day must end that work the ides
           of March begun. And whether we shall meet again I know not;
           for ever, and for ever, farewell, Cassius! If we do meet again,
           why, we shall smile; if not, why then this parting was well
           made.

CASSIUS   For ever, and for ever, farewell, Brutus! If we do meet again, we'll smile indeed; if not, 'tis true this parting was well made.

They ride away, together at first, then parting, one to the left, the other right.

The legions march towards one another. Then comes the clash of their meeting. There is violent fighting. The world is full of blood and dust, and the sounds of screams and howls, and blazing trumpets. All day long the battle raged. At last, the sun went down at Philippi. Antony and Octavius were victorious.

PINDARUS   Fly further off my lord. Mark Antony is in your tents.

CASSIUS   This day I breathed first; this is come round, and where I did begin, there shall I end. Caesar, thou art reveng'd, even with the sword that kill'd thee.

The battlefield darkens. Brutus bends over the dead body of Cassius who has killed himself rather than be captured.

The ghost of Caesar appears briefly and then fades away.

BRUTUS   O Julius Caesar, thou art mighty yet. (*He stares down.*) The last of all the Romans, fare thee well! Friends, I owe more tears to this dead man than you shall see me pay. I shall find time, Cassius, I shall find time. (*They all sit down.*) Our enemies have beat us to the pit. It is more worthy to leap in ourselves than tarry till they push us.

There are shouts in the distance and the approach of glimmer-ing torches. Brutus bids farewell to his friends, all of whom leave save one, an old soldier by name of Strato.

BRUTUS   I know my hour is come. (*He runs on his sword.*) Caesar, now be still, I killed not thee with half so good a will.

He dies. The torches draw near.

The victorious Romans, Antony and Octavius, come upon the dead body of Brutus with Strato guarding it.

ANTONY   How died thy master, Strato?

STRATO   Brutus only overcame himself, and no man else hath honour by his death.

ANTONY   (*to Brutus*) This was the noblest Roman of them all: all the conspirators, save only he, did that they did in envy of great Caesar. He only, in a general honest thought and common good to all, made one of them. His life was gentle, and the elements so mixed in him that Nature might stand up and say to all the world, 'This was a man'.

The curtain falls.

AS YOU LIKE IT

As You Like It tells a story that begins in the discord and violence of a tyrant's court, where broken ribs and brotherly hatred are the orders of the day, and moves to the strange, enchanted Forest of Arden, where all wounds are healed and all ills made good, where the very trees sprout love-poems … It is a forest fairly infested with wandering lovers and outlaws who 'live like the old Robin Hood of England … and fleet the time carelessly, as they did in the golden world.'

It is indeed a golden play, and at the very heart of it is Rosalind, a banished princess, who, with her companions in exile, seeks the young Orlando, who, as her cousin puts it, "tripped up the wrestler's heels, and your heart, both in an instant!"

LEON GARFIELD

The curtain rises on a lawn before the palace. There is to be a wrestling match before Duke Frederick and all his court. Already Charles, the strongest man in the country, has broken the ribs of three young men; now a fourth is awaited. Celia, the daughter of the duke, and Rosalind her cousin enter. They are followed by the duke and his courtiers, together with Charles the wrestler and Orlando, the fourth young man.

DUKE   How now, daughter and Rosalind? Are you crept hither to see
          the wrestling?

ROSALIND Ay, uncle, so please you give us leave.

DUKE   You will take little delight in it, I can tell you, there is such
          odds in the man. In pity of the challenger's youth I would fain
          dissuade him, but he will not be entreated.

          *Duke Frederick gives a sign and Charles and Orlando begin to
          wrestle. The girls exclaim while watching.*

ROSALIND Now Hercules be thy speed, young man!

CELIA   I would I were invisible, to catch the strong fellow by the leg!

          Charles is thrown.

ROSALIND O excellent young man!

          *Shouts of amazement and admiration. Only one man hides
          himself angrily in the crowd – Oliver, Orlando's brother, who
          hates him.*

DUKE   (*to Orlando*) What is thy name, young man?

ORLANDO   Orlando, my liege, the youngest son of Sir Rowland de Boys.

DUKE   I would thou hadst been son to some man else; the world esteem'd thy father honourable, but I did find him still mine enemy.

The duke departs barely suppressing his anger, followed by his court. Rosalind and Celia remain with Orlando.

CELIA   My father's rough and envious disposition sticks me at the heart. (*They approach Orlando.*)

ROSALIND   (*giving him a chain from her neck*) Gentleman, wear this for me; one out of suits with Fortune, that could give more, but that her hand lacks means.

Orlando is tongue-tied. Plainly, he and Rosalind have fallen in love. Celia leads Rosalind away. Orlando gazes after them, enraptured.

Rosalind and Celia are together in their apartment.

CELIA   Come, come, wrestle with thy affections.

The duke enters furiously.

DUKE   Mistress, dispatch you with your safest haste, and get you from our court!

ROSALIND   Me, uncle?

DUKE   You, cousin. Within these ten days if that thou be'st found so near our public court as twenty miles, thou diest for it!

ROSALIND   I do beseech your Grace, let me the knowledge of my fault bear with me.

DUKE   Thou art thy father's daughter, there's enough.

He storms out.

CELIA   O my poor Rosalind, whither wilt thou go? Wilt thou change fathers? I will give thee mine. Say what thou canst, I'll go along with thee.

ROSALIND   Why, whither shall we go?

CELIA   To seek my uncle in the forest of Arden.

ROSALIND   Alas, what danger will it be to us? (*An idea seems to have struck Rosalind . . .*) But what if we assay'd . . .

Eagerly, they dress themselves for their adventure; Celia as a country maiden and Rosalind as a youth. They persuade Touchstone, the duke's jester, to bear them company in the forest.

CELIA   What shall I call thee when thou art a man?

ROSALIND   (*coming back in and putting on a hat*) Call me Ganymede. But what will you be called?

CELIA   (*coming in and putting on an apron*) No longer Celia, but Aliena.

In the forest of Arden Rosalind's father, once duke, but driven out by his younger brother Frederick, lives in banishment with a few faithful friends.

DUKE SENIOR   Now my brothers in exile, hath not old custom made this life more sweet than that of painted pomp? Are not these woods more free from peril than the envious court? And this our life finds tongues in trees, books in the running brooks, and good in everything. Where is Jaques?

LORD   We today did steal behind him as he lay under an oak, to which place a poor stag, that from the hunter's aim had ta'en a hurt, did come to languish. He swears that we are mere usurpers, tyrants, and what's worse, fright the animals and kill them in their native dwelling-place.

DUKE SENIOR   Show me the place. I love to hear him in these sullen fits.

The duke and lords ride off.

Orlando returns to his home and finds Adam, his old servant, waiting for him at the door.

ADAM   O unhappy youth, come not within these doors! Your brother hath heard your praises, and this night he means to burn the lodging where you use to lie, and you within it.

ORLANDO   Why, whither, Adam, wouldst thou have me go? Wouldst thou have me go and beg my food? Or with a base and boist'rous sword enforce a thievish living on the common road?

ADAM   But do not so! I have five hundred crowns I saved under your father. Take that.

ORLANDO   O good old man.

ADAM   Let me go with you. Though I look old, yet I am strong and lusty.

ORLANDO   Come, we'll go along together.

The three travellers, Rosalind, Celia and Touchstone, limp miserably through the forest. Rosalind, being dressed as a man, feels it her duty to present a bold and cheerful appearance.

ROSALIND   Well, this is the forest of Arden.

TOUCHSTONE   Ay, now am I in Arden, the more fool I. When I was at home, I was in a better place.

ROSALIND   Look you, who comes here.

They withdraw into concealment as Corin, an old shepherd and Silvius enter.

SILVIUS   O Corin, that thou knew'st how I do love her!

CORIN   I partly guess; for I have loved ere now.

SILVIUS   No, Corin, being old, thou canst not guess. O Phebe, Phebe, Phebe!

Silvius wanders away, distracted.

ROSALIND   Jove, Jove! This shepherd's passion is much upon my fashion! *(Rosalind leaves the shelter of the trees and approaches Corin.)* Good even to you, friend.

CORIN   And to you, gentle sir, and to you all.

ROSALIND   I prithee, shepherd, bring us where we may rest ourselves and feed. Here's a young maid with travel much oppress'd, and faints for succour.

CORIN   Fair sir, I pity her; but I am shepherd to another man. His cottage, flocks, and bounds of feed are now on sale, and there is nothing that you will feed on –

ROSALIND   I pray thee, if it stands with honesty, buy thou the cottage, pasture, and the flock, and thou shalt have to pay for it of us.

CELIA   And we will mend thy wages.

CORIN   I will your very faithful feeder be.

Another part of the forest. Orlando appears, assisting his old servant.

ADAM   Dear master, I can go no further. O, I die for food. Here lie I down and measure out my grave. Farewell, kind master.

ORLANDO   Why, how now, Adam? No greater heart in thee? Live a little, comfort a little, cheer thyself a little. If this uncouth forest yield anything savage, I will be either food for it, or bring it for food to thee.

Orlando unsheaths his sword and goes further into the forest. Hearing rustling in the grass, he stops and hides behind the bushes. A hound runs out and then runs deeper into the forest. Orlando follows the dog. He hears a song in the distance.

AMIENS   Under the greenwood tree
Who loves to lie with me,
And turn his merry note
Unto the sweet bird's throat,
Come hither, come hither, come hither!
Here shall he see
No enemy
But winter and rough weather.

He follows the 'Come hither', towards a glimmering of light and creeps to look between the foliage. The scene before him is of a banquet, lantern lit, and surrounded by gentlemen in comfortable furs. Among them is the melancholy Jaques. A hound lies at the feet of Duke Senior. The duke is about to sip from a goblet when he is interrupted.

ORLANDO   (*rushing forward with drawn sword*) Forbear, and eat no more!

JAQUES   Why, I have eat none yet.

ORLANDO   Nor shalt not, till necessity be served.

DUKE SENIOR   Sit down and feed, and welcome to our table.

ORLANDO   (*putting up his sword*) Speak you so gently? Pardon me, I pray you. I thought that all things had been savage here. There is an old poor man —

DUKE SENIOR   Go find him out, and we will nothing waste till your return.

ORLANDO   (*departing*) I thank ye.

DUKE SENIOR   Thou seest we are not all alone unhappy: this wide and universal theatre presents more woeful pageants than the scene wherein we play.

JAQUES   All the world's a stage and all the men and women merely players. They have their exits and their entrances, and one man in his time plays many parts, his acts being seven ages. At first the infant . . . then the whining schoolboy . . . and then the lover. Then a soldier, jealous in honour, sudden, and quick in quarrel, and then the justice. The sixth age shifts into the lean and slipper'd pantaloon, with spectacles on nose. Last scene of all that ends this history, is second childishness, sans teeth, sans eyes, sans taste, sans everything.

As Jaques finishes his monologue, Orlando returns with Adam who is warmly welcomed, as if in contradiction of Jaques' grim view of old age.

At the palace, Duke Frederick discovers his daughter's flight with Rosalind; and, having heard of their talk with Orlando, suspects that they have all fled together. In a rage, he sends for Oliver, and orders him to find his brother Orlando or risk banishment himself.

In the forest Orlando has decorated all the trees he can find with poems of love to Rosalind.

ORLANDO   Hang there my verse, in witness of my love.

And away he goes in search of still more trees. No sooner has he gone than Rosalind appears with a poem in her hand.

ROSALIND   'From the east to western Inde,
                            No jewel is like Rosalind.
                            All the pictures fairest lin'd
                            Are but black to Rosalind.
                            Let no face be kept in mind
                            But the fair of Rosalind'.

Enter Celia, with another poem.

CELIA   'Thus Rosalind of many parts,
          By heavenly synod was devis'd,
          Of many faces, eyes, and hearts . . .'

TOUCHSTONE (*peeping out from behind a tree*) This is the very false gallop of verses; why do you infect yourself with them?

ROSALIND Peace, you dull fool! I found them on a tree.

TOUCHSTONE Truly, the tree yields bad fruit.

He disappears. Celia holds out her paper to Rosalind.

CELIA   Trow you who hath done this?

ROSALIND   Is it a man?

CELIA   It is young Orlando that tripped up the wrestler's heels and your heart, both in an instant.

ROSALIND   Alas the day, what shall I do with my doublet and hose? How looked he?

CELIA   Soft, comes he not here?

They retire into concealment. Orlando and Jaques appear.

JAQUES   Rosalind is your love's name?

ORLANDO   Yes, just.

JAQUES   I do not like her name.

ORLANDO   There was no thought of pleasing you when she was christened.

JAQUES   What stature is she of?

ORLANDO   Just as high as my heart.

JAQUES   You are full of pretty answers. Farewell, good Signior Love.

Jaques goes off in disgust. Rosalind leans forward. Orlando is whittling a boat.

ROSALIND   I pray you, what is't o'clock?

ORLANDO   You should ask me what time o' day. There is no clock in the forest.

He puts his boat into the brook. A sheet with verses is the sail. Rosalind throws a pebble at the boat.

ORLANDO   (*angrily*) What would you?

ROSALIND   (*jumps down from her branch and points to a tree carved with 'Rosalind'*) There is a man haunts the forest, that abuses our young plants, hangs odes upon hawthorns and elegies on brambles, all deifying the name of Rosalind. If I could meet that fancy-monger, I would give him some good counsel.

ORLANDO   I am he that is so love-shaked.

ROSALIND   Love is merely a madness; yet I profess curing it by counsel.

ORLANDO   Did you ever cure any so?

ROSALIND   Yes, one, and in this manner. He was to imagine me his love, his mistress; and I set him every day to woo me. At which time would I grieve, be proud, fantastical, apish, inconstant, full of tears, full of smiles, that I drave my suitor from his mad humour of love to a living humour of madness. And thus I cured him.

ORLANDO   I would not be cured, youth.

ROSALIND   I would cure you, if you would but call me Rosalind, and come every day to my cote and woo me.

Love grows in the forest fast as weeds. Even Touchstone has found himself a mate, and being of the spirit, he has mocked even himself with his choice. He has found a true country lass, as thick as mud.

TOUCHSTONE   I will fetch up your goats, Audrey, as another poet did. Truly, I wish the gods had made thee poetical.

AUDREY   I do not know what 'poetical' is. Is it honest?

TOUCHSTONE   No truly; for the truest poetry is the most feigning.

AUDREY   Well, I am not fair, and therefore I pray the gods make me honest.

TOUCHSTONE   Truly, and to cast away honesty upon a foul slut were to put good meat into an unclean dish. But be it as it may be, I will marry thee.

Nearby their cottage, Rosalind and Celia await Orlando. He is late.

ROSALIND   Never talk to me, I will weep.

CELIA   Do, but consider that tears do not become a man.

ROSALIND   Why did he swear he would come this morning, and comes not?

CELIA   Nay certainly there is no truth in him.

ROSALIND   Not true in love? You have heard him swear he was.

CELIA   'Was' is not 'is'.

Old Corin approaches.

CORIN Mistress and master, you have oft enquired after the shepherd that complained of love –

CELIA Well, and what of him?

Corin, with his finger to his lips, beckons. They creep forward, part some foliage and observe Silvius and his Phebe.

SILVIUS Sweet Phebe, do not scorn me, do not Phebe! If ever you meet in some fresh cheek the power of fancy, then shall you know the wounds invisible that love's keen arrows make.

PHEBE But till that time, come not thou near me; and when that time comes, afflict me with thy mocks, pity me not, as till that time, I shall not pity thee.

SILVIUS Oh!

ROSALIND (*coming forward*) And why, I pray you? Who might be your mother, that you insult, exult, and all at once, over the wretched? You foolish shepherd, wherefore do you follow her? Mistress, know yourself. Down on your knees, and thank heaven fasting for a good man's love; for I must tell you friendly in your ear, sell when you can, you are not for all markets.

PHEBE   Sweet youth, I pray you chide a year together, I had rather hear you chide than this man woo.

ROSALIND   I pray you do not fall in love with me, for I am falser than vows made in wine. (*She leaves.*)

PHEBE   (*gazing after Rosalind*) Who ever loved that loved not at first sight?

In another part of the forest. Rosalind is standing on a bridge across the brook. At last, Orlando arrives.

ORLANDO   My fair Rosalind, I come within an hour of my promise.

ROSALIND   Break an hour's promise in love!

ORLANDO   Pardon me, dear Rosalind.

ROSALIND   Nay, and you be so tardy, come no more in my sight. I had as lief been wooed of a snail. Am not I your Rosalind?

ORLANDO   I would take some joy to say you are, because I would be talking of her.

ROSALIND   Well, in her person, I say I will not have you.

ORLANDO   Then in mine own person, I die.

ROSALIND   No, faith, men have died from time to time, and worms have
           eaten them, but not for love. But come now, I will be your
           Rosalind in a more coming-on disposition; and ask me what
           you will, I will grant it.

ORLANDO   Then love me, Rosalind.

ROSALIND   Ay, and twenty such. Now tell me how long you would have
           her after you have possessed her.

ORLANDO   For ever and a day.

ROSALIND   Say 'a day' without the 'ever'. No, no, Orlando, men are April
           when they woo, December when they wed; maids are May
           when they are maids, but the sky changes when they are wives.

ORLANDO   But will my Rosalind do so?

ROSALIND   By my life, she will do as I do.

           The sound of a horn is heard.

ORLANDO   I must attend the duke at dinner. For these two hours I will
           leave thee. Adieu.

           He departs. Celia appears from behind a tree.

CELIA   You have simply misused our sex in your love-prate.

ROSALIND   (*taking off her hat, fluffing out her hair, and lying on the grass*)
           O coz, coz, coz, my pretty little coz, that thou didst know how
           many fathom deep I am in love!

There is yet another victim of Duke Frederick's fury in the forest. Oliver de Boys, sent to fetch his brother, has wandered, lost and wretched, till at last he lies down to rest. As he sleeps, a lioness approaches. Then it is that Orlando, coming upon his brother, and seeing his danger, fights with the lioness and overcomes it. But in so doing, Orlando is wounded himself. Faint from loss of blood, he sends Oliver to keep his appointment with the shepherd boy. All enmity between the brothers is now ended.

OLIVER   Good morrow, fair ones. Orlando doth commend him to you both. He sent me hither, stranger as I am, to tell this story, that you might excuse his broken promise, and to give this napkin, dy'd in his blood, unto the shepherd youth that he in sport doth call his Rosalind.

He holds out the napkin. Rosalind faints.

CELIA   Why, how now, Ganymede, sweet Ganymede?

Celia and Oliver rush to help Rosalind up, but bump their heads together and, blushing, stare at each other.

OLIVER   Many will swoon when they do look on blood.

ROSALIND   I would I were at home.

They help her back to the cottage.

There is a haystack in a clearing. Voices come from it.

TOUCHSTONE   We shall find a time, Audrey, patience, gentle Audrey.

CORIN   (*entering and knocking on the haystack*) Our master and mistress seeks you. Come away, away!

TOUCHSTONE   (*to Audrey, who has run out and is putting herself in order*) Trip, Audrey, trip Audrey! I attend, I attend.

A clearing in the forest. Oliver and Orlando are together. Orlando's arm is in a sling.

ORLANDO   Is't possible that on so little acquaintance you should like her?

OLIVER   I love Aliena; she loves me; consent with both that we may enjoy each other. My father's house and all the revenue that was old Sir Rowland's will I estate upon you, and here live and die a shepherd.

ORLANDO   Let your wedding be tomorrow; thither will I invite the duke and all's contented followers.

Off goes Oliver, delighted. Rosalind appears.

ROSALIND   O my dear Orlando, how it grieves me to see thee wear thy heart in a scarf.

ORLANDO   It is my arm.

ROSALIND   Did your brother tell you how well I counterfeited to swoon when he showed me your handkercher?

ORLANDO   Ay, and greater wonders than that.

ROSALIND   O, I know where you are. Nay, 'tis true. Your brother and my sister are in the very wrath of love.

ORLANDO   They shall be married tomorrow. But O, how bitter a thing it is to look into happiness through another man's eyes!

ROSALIND   Why then tomorrow I cannot serve your turn for Rosalind?

ORLANDO   I can no longer live by thinking.

ROSALIND   (*mysteriously*) I can do strange things. Put you in your best array, bid your friends; for if you will be married tomorrow, you shall; and to Rosalind, if you will.

Silvius and Phebe appear.

PHEBE   Youth, you have done me much ungentleness –

ROSALIND   I care not if I have. You are there followed by a faithful shepherd – look upon him, love him; he worships you.

PHEBE   Good shepherd, tell this youth what 'tis to love.

SILVIUS   It is to be all made of sighs and tears, and so am I for Phebe.

PHEBE   And I for Ganymede.

ORLANDO   And I for Rosalind.

ROSALIND   And I for no woman.

SILVIUS   It is to be all made of faith and service, and so am I for Phebe.

PHEBE   And I for Ganymede.

ORLANDO   And I for Rosalind.

ROSALIND   And I for no woman.

SILVIUS   It is to be all made of fantasy, all made of passion –

ROSALIND   Pray you no more of this, 'tis like the howling of Irish wolves against the moon! (*To Phebe*) I will marry you if ever I marry woman, and I'll be married tomorrow. But if you do refuse to marry me, you'll give yourself to this most faithful shepherd.

PHEBE   So is the bargain.

ROSALIND   Keep your word; from hence I go to make these doubts all even. Tomorrow meet me all together.

The morning sun breaks through into a clearing. A flute plays. Duke Senior, Jaques, Orlando, Oliver and Celia are waiting.

AMIENS   (*singing*)   It was a lover and his lass,
With a hey and a ho and a hey nonino,
That o'er the green corn-field did pass,
In spring-time, the only pretty ring-time,
When birds do sing, hey ding a ding, ding,
Sweet lovers love the spring.

DUKE SENIOR   Dost thou believe, Orlando, that Ganymede
can do all this that he hath promised?

ORLANDO   I sometimes do believe, and sometimes do not.

Touchstone and Audrey, Silvius and Phebe enter.

JAQUES   There is sure another flood toward, and these couples are coming to the ark.

TOUCHSTONE   I press in here, sir, to swear and forswear, according as marriage binds and blood breaks. (*Pushing Audrey forward*) A poor virgin, sir, an ill-favoured thing, sir, but mine own.

Hymen enters.

HYMEN   Good Duke, receive thy daughter,
Hymen from heaven brought her,
That thou mightst join her hand with his
Whose heart within his bosom is.

He beckons and Rosalind, now dressed as herself, appears.

ROSALIND   (*to duke*) To you I give myself, for I am yours.
(*To Orlando*) To you I give myself for I am yours.

DUKE SENIOR   If there be truth in sight, you are my daughter.

ORLANDO   If there be truth in sight, you are my Rosalind.

PHEBE   If sight and shape be true, why then my love adieu!

HYMEN   Here's eight that must take hands,
              To join in Hymen's bands.
              (*To Orlando and Rosalind*)
              You and you no cross shall part.
              (*To Oliver and Celia*)
              You and you are heart in heart.
              (*To Phebe*)
              You to his love must accord,
              Or have a woman for your lord.
              (*To Touchstone and Audrey*)
              You and you are sure together,
              As the winter to foul weather.

The couples embrace. A messenger enters.

MESSENGER   Let me have audience for a word or two. Duke Frederick
              addressed a mighty power to take his brother here, and to the
              skirts of this wild wood he came. Meeting with an old religious
              man, he was converted from his enterprise and from the world,
              his crown bequeathing to his banished brother.

DUKE SENIOR   Every of this happy number that have endur'd shrewd days and nights with us, shall share the good of our returned fortune . . . Play, music, and you brides and bridegrooms all, with measure heap'd in joy, to th' measures fall!

As the curtain falls, the couples pass before the spectators in joyful dancing.

KING RICHARD III

The Tragedy of King Richard III is the story of a royal monster, a misshapen
devil by name of Richard, Duke of Gloucester. At the very beginning of the
play, Shakespeare seems to hurl him onto the stage so that he limps and stumbles out of the shadows, almost unwillingly into the light. "I am determined
to prove a villain," he confides; and does so with a vengeance as he claws his
bloody way to the throne, murdering all who stand in his path, even little
children: "I fear no uncles dead," says one of his nephews. "Nor none that
live, I hope," protests his murderous uncle, and sends the child and his little
brother to their deaths in the grim Tower of London. At length, even his own
mother is driven to curse him: "Bloody thou art, bloody will be thy end!"
And so it is.

LEON GARFIELD

The curtain rises on the Palace of Westminster, dark against a bloodshot sky. A black misshapen figure crawls up onto the battlements and, like a malevolent spider, crouches over the town below.

RICHARD   Now is the winter of our discontent made glorious summer by this son of York.

The winter of discontent is the long civil war between the houses of York and Lancaster. The glorious son of York is the victor King Edward IV, and the speaker is his brother Richard Duke of Gloucester.

RICHARD   But I that am deform'd, unfinish'd, have no delight to pass away the time, and therefore, since I cannot prove a lover, I am determined to prove a villain . . .

King Edward is sick; and so is the kingdom. Fear, greed, treachery and hatred set family against family, mother against son, and brother against brother. A fierce ambition burns in the dark heart of the king's hunchback brother: he will be king! Already he has murdered Henry VI and his son, Edward, but others of his own family still stand in his way, even his brother George, Duke of Clarence.

Along a stony passageway comes the Duke of Clarence, between armed guards. Suddenly the figure of Richard emerges from the darkness and stands in the way.

RICHARD	Brother, good day; what means this armed guard?
CLARENCE	His majesty hath appointed this conduct to convey me to the Tower.
RICHARD	Upon what cause?
CLARENCE	Because my name is George. A wizard told him that by 'G' his issue disinherited should be. And for my name of George begins with 'G', it follows in his thought that I am he.
RICHARD	Brother, farewell. I will unto the king. Your imprisonment shall not be long; I will deliver you, or else lie for you.

Clarence is marched away by the guard. Richard, smiling, stares after them. He rubs his hands with complicity.

RICHARD   Go, tread the path that thou shalt ne'er return; I do love thee so that I will shortly send thy soul to Heaven –

Richard is in his apartment, preening himself before a mirror. He puts on his rings, admiring the glitter of the precious stones. He is one step nearer. But he needs to be respectable, he needs a well-born wife, and who better than the Lady Anne?

A noise outside attracts Richard's attention. He sees from his window Lady Anne in mourning and gentlemen with halberds, following a coffin. The procession stops in front of his windows.

RICHARD   (*stepping back from the window*) I'll marry Warwick's youngest daughter. What though I kill'd her husband and her father?

ANNE   (*gazing at the coffin.*) Poor key-cold figure of a holy king . . . be it lawful that I invoke thy ghost to hear the lamentations of poor Anne.

Suddenly a huge shadow falls over her. Anne turns around. Richard appears in front of the procession.

RICHARD   Villains, set down the corse!

The bearers lower the coffin and retreat in fear.

ANNE   Foul devil, for God's sake hence, and trouble us not.

RICHARD   Sweet saint, for charity, be not so curst.

ANNE   (*to bearers*) O gentlemen! see, see dead Henry's wounds open their congeal'd mouths and bleed afresh! Blush, blush thou lump of foul deformity, for 'tis thy presence that exhales this blood!

RICHARD   Lady, you know no rules of charity –

ANNE   Villain, thou know'st no law of God nor man! Didst thou not kill this king?

RICHARD   (*coming closer to Anne and speaking softly*) I grant ye. The better for the King of Heaven, that hath him.

ANNE   And thou unfit for any place but hell.

RICHARD   (*going around Anne*) Yes, one place else.

ANNE   Some dungeon?

RICHARD   (*stopping in front of Anne*) Your bed-chamber.

ANNE   (*spitting at him*) Out of my sight!

RICHARD   Your beauty was the cause, your beauty, that did haunt me in my sleep to undertake the death of all the world.

ANNE   (*covering her face with her hands*) If I thought that, I tell thee, homicide, these nails should rend that beauty from my cheeks.

RICHARD   Teach not thy lip such scorn; for it was made for kissing, lady, not for such contempt. If thy revengeful heart cannot forgive, lo, here I lend thee this sharp-pointed sword.

He kneels and, offering his sword, bares his breast. She takes the sword but, trembling, cannot strike the blow.

RICHARD   Nay, do not pause; for I did kill King Henry, but 'twas thy beauty that provoked me. Nay, now dispatch; 'twas I that stabb'd young Edward, but 'twas thy heavenly face that set me on. Take up the sword again, or take up me.

ANNE   I would I knew thy heart.

RICHARD   Vouchsafe to wear this ring.

Richard takes Anne's hand and puts a ring on her finger.

ANNE   To take is not to give.

RICHARD   Look how my ring encompasseth thy finger; even so thy breast encloseth my poor heart.

The procession departs, leaving Richard alone. He hops along, well pleased with himself, and his long misshapen shadow accompanies him.

RICHARD   (*to shadow*) Was ever woman in this humour woo'd? Was ever woman in this humour won? I'll have her, but I will not keep her long.

In the semi-darkness of King Edward's bedchamber the queen and relatives stand about his bed. Richard looks in and sees the queen make a few steps and kneel in front of a crucifix. The king's sickness has deepened and the queen is full of dread. Should he die, her sons are too young to rule. With George, Duke of Clarence, in the Tower, Richard, the third brother, will be Protector. And the venomous hunchback hates her and her family.

RICHARD   He cannot live, I hope, and must not die till George be pack'd with post-horse up to Heaven.

In a small, gloomy room in the Tower, lit by moonlight coming through the narrow windows, the Duke of Clarence lies upon his bed. His sleep is uneasy. Shadows fall across his face. He wakes. Two murderers stare down on him.

CLARENCE   In God's name, what art thou?

1ST MURDERER   A man, as you are.

CLARENCE   Who sent you hither? Wherefore do you come?

2ND MURDERER   To –

CLARENCE   To murder me? (*They nod.*) Wherein, my friends have I offended you?

1ST MURDERER   Offended us you have not, but the king; therefore prepare to die.

CLARENCE   I will send you to my brother Gloucester who shall reward you better for my life than Edward will for tidings of my death.

2ND MURDERER   You are deceiv'd: your brother Gloucester hates you.

1ST MURDERER   'Tis he that sends us to destroy you here.

He struggles from his bed and holds out his hands, pleadingly, to second murderer. The first murderer stabs him, and pushes him head first into a malmsey-butt to drown in a nightmare of crimson bubbles.

A black flag flies above the palace. Richard has murdered his brother Clarence only just in time; King Edward is dead. All that remains between the hunchback and the crown is the problem of the king's two sons, the little princes. Desperately, the queen sends her own brothers to Ludlow to secure her children's safety, before it is too late. But Richard has a clever friend, his cousin, the Duke of Buckingham who advises they should not be tardy in seizing the heir to the throne.

BUCKINGHAM My lord, whoever journeys to the prince, for God's sake let not us two stay at home.

RICHARD My dear cousin, I as a child will go by thy direction. Towards Ludlow then.

The queen's brothers are seized by Richard's men and put to death and Edward, the little Prince of Wales, is brought to London. Hearing this terrible news, the queen decides to go with her younger son, the Duke of York, into sanctuary. Her friend, the Archbishop of York, leads them there.

ELIZABETH (*clutching her youngest child*) Ay me! I see the ruin of our house: the tiger now hath seiz'd the gentle hind! Come, come, my boy; we will to sanctuary.

At the palace, Richard, Buckingham and others await the arrival of the Prince of Wales. As soon as he arrives, Richard, hopping and capering, like a genial uncle, comes forward to greet him. Buckingham follows Richard.

RICHARD   Welcome, dear cousin, the weary way hath made you melancholy.

EDWARD   No uncle; but our crosses on the way have made it tedious. (*He looks around him.*) I thought my mother and my brother York would long ere this have met us on the way. (*He turns to a nobleman, Lord Hastings.*) Welcome my lord. What, will our mother come?

HASTINGS	(*bowing*) The queen your mother and your brother York have taken sanctuary.
BUCKINGHAM	Fie, what an indirect and peevish course is this of hers! Lord Cardinal, will your grace persuade the queen to send the Duke of York unto his princely brother presently?
ARCHBISHOP	God in Heaven forbid we should infringe the sacred privilege of blessed sanctuary!
BUCKINGHAM	Oft have I heard of sanctuary men, but sanctuary children, never till now.

The cardinal and Hastings leave.

EDWARD	Good lords, make all the speedy haste you may. (*To Richard*) Say, uncle Gloucester, if our brother come, where shall we sojourn till our coronation?
RICHARD	If I may counsel you, some day or two your Highness shall repose you at the Tower.
EDWARD	I do not like the Tower.
BUCKINGHAM	Now in good time here comes the Duke of York.

The young Duke of York, accompanied by Hastings and the cardinal, appears.

EDWARD	Richard of York! how fares our loving brother?

YORK   Well, my lord.

RICHARD   How fares our cousin, noble lord of York?

YORK   I thank you, gentle uncle.

RICHARD   (*to Edward*) My lord, will't please you pass along? Myself will to your mother, to entreat of her to meet you at the Tower.

YORK   (*to his brother*) What, will you go unto the Tower, my lord?

EDWARD   My Lord Protector needs will have it so.

YORK   I shall not sleep in quiet at the Tower.

RICHARD   Why, what should you fear?

YORK   My uncle Clarence' angry ghost: my grandam told me he was murder'd there.

EDWARD   I fear no uncles dead.

RICHARD   Nor none that live, I hope?

The princes leave for the Tower that looms ahead, like a crouching monster. Richard and Buckingham stare after the procession. They see it disappear behind the gates of the fortress, the ravens circling above it. Richard rubs his hands with satisfaction.

With the two little princes, like birds in a cage, locked up in the Tower, Richard's way to the throne is clear. But before he can proclaim himself king, he needs the assent of Lord Hastings, the Lord Chamberlain.

BUCKINGHAM   What shall we do if we perceive Lord Hastings will not yield to our complots?

RICHARD   Chop off his head, man! (*He laughs and lays his arm upon Buckingham's shoulder.*) When I am king, claim thou of me the earldom of Hereford.

BUCKINGHAM   I'll claim that promise at your grace's hand.

In the middle of the night, Sir William Catesby, another friend of Richard's, is sent to rouse Lord Hastings from his bed and sound him out.

HASTINGS   What news, what news in this our tott'ring state?

CATESBY   It is a reeling world indeed, my lord, and will never stand upright till Richard wear the garland of the realm.

HASTINGS   Dost thou mean the crown?

CATESBY   Ay, my good lord.

HASTINGS   I'll have this crown of mine cut from my shoulders before I'll see the crown so foul misplac'd!

CATESBY   God keep your lordship in that gracious mind. (*He hides a grim smile.*)

Lord Hastings is invited to dinner in the Tower. He supposes it is to fix the day for the crowning of little Prince Edward as England's rightful king. Why else should Richard, the Lord Protector, summon him? Seated at the table, he finds Ely, Buckingham and other nobles.

HASTINGS   Now, noble peers, the cause why we are met is to determine of the coronation. When is the royal day?

ELY   Tomorrow is I judge a happy day.

BUCKINGHAM   Who knows the Lord Protector's mind herein?

ELY.   Your grace, we think, should soonest know his mind.

BUCKINGHAM   Lord Hastings, you and he are near in love.

HASTINGS   I thank his grace, I know he loves me well; but for his purpose in the coronation I have not sounded him. But you, my honourable lords, may name the time, and in the duke's behalf I'll give my voice –

ELY   In happy time, here comes the duke himself!

RICHARD   (*entering, all affable*) My noble lords and cousins all, good morrow!

BUCKINGHAM   Had you not come upon your cue, my lord, William, Lord Hastings had pronounc'd your part – I mean your voice for crowning of the king.

RICHARD   Than my Lord Hastings, no man might be bolder! My Lord of Ely, when I was last in Holborn I saw good strawberries in your garden there; I do beseech you, send for some of them!

ELY   Marry, and will, my lord, with all my heart! (*He leaves to send for some.*)

RICHARD   Cousin of Buckingham, a word with you. (*They leave the table together.*)

ELY   (*returning*) Where is the Duke of Gloucester? I have sent for these strawberries.

HASTINGS   His grace looks cheerfully and smooth this morning; there's some conceit or other likes him well. I think there's never a man in Christendom can lesser hide his love or hate than he, for by his face straight shall you know his heart.

Richard returns with Buckingham. Buckingham is looking troubled, Richard savage.

RICHARD   I pray you all, tell me what they deserve that do conspire my death with devilish plots of damned witchcraft, and that have prevail'd upon my body with their hellish charms?

HASTINGS   I say, my lord, they have deserved death.

RICHARD   Then be your eyes the witness of their evil! (*Drags up a sleeve to show his withered arm.*) See how I am bewitch'd! And this is Edward's wife, that monstrous witch, consorted with that harlot, strumpet Shore, that by their witchcraft thus have marked me!

HASTINGS   If they have done this deed, my noble lord –

RICHARD   If? Thou protector of this damned strumpet, talk'st thou to me
           of ifs? Thou art a traitor: off with his head! Now by Saint Paul
           I will not dine until I see the same.

*Richard storms out, and is followed by the others, leaving the
dismayed Hastings. Two sinister figures of the guard appear
behind him. One of them puts his hand on Hasting's shoulder
and squeezes it. Hastings lowers his head realizing that he is
doomed. He is led away.*

A servant enters the room bearing a dish of strawberries that he places on the table. The other nobles return with Richard and Buckingham. They seat themselves and dishes are brought in. A covered plate is set before Richard. He lifts the lid. Hastings' severed head glares out. Silence falls upon the table.

RICHARD   (*sighing*) So dear I lov'd the man that I must weep. (*He bows his head.*)

BUCKINGHAM   (*jumping up*) Long live King Richard, England's worthy king!

LORDS   Long live King Richard!

At last the hunchback, having climbed a ladder of murders, is king. But while he walks in glory, three women stand in wretchedness and grief before the Tower. Richard's unhappy wife, the Lady Anne; the queen, mother of the two little princes; and the mother of the hunchback himself, the Duchess of York.

DUCHESS   O my accursed womb, the bed of death! A cockatrice hast thou hatch'd to the world, whose unavoided eye is murderous!

ANNE   He hates me . . . and will, no doubt, shortly be rid of me.

QUEEN   Pity, you ancient stones, those tender babes. Rough cradle for such little pretty ones! Use my babies well.

In the great hall of the palace, thronged with nobles, King Richard, crowned and robed, hops between the bowing figures. His cloak is huge and scarlet and flows after him like a river of blood. He ascends the throne and beckons to Buckingham who comes to kneel beside him.

RICHARD	Shall we wear these glories for a day? Or shall they last?
BUCKINGHAM	For ever let them last!
RICHARD	(*shaking his head*) Young Edward lives – think now what I would speak.
BUCKINGHAM	Say on, my loving lord.
RICHARD	Cousin, thou wast not wont to be so dull. Shall I be plain? I wish the bastards dead. What say'st thou now?
BUCKINGHAM	Your grace may do your pleasure.
RICHARD	Tut, tut, thou art all ice. Say, have I thy consent that they shall die?
BUCKINGHAM	Give me some little breath, some pause, before I positively speak in this.

Bowing, Buckingham withdraws. Richard stares after him, malevolently.

| RICHARD | High-reaching Buckingham grows circumspect. (*He beckons to a page, who approaches. Richard murmurs in his ear.*) Know'st thou not any whom corrupting gold will tempt unto a close exploit of death? (*The page nods and hastens away. Richard glares about him. He sees Buckingham smiling. He smiles in return.*) No more shall he be neighbour to my counsels. Come hither, Catesby! Rumour it abroad that Anne, my wife, is very grievous sick. (*Catesby looks startled.*) I say again, give out that Anne, my queen, is sick and like to die. About it! (*Catesby departs.*) |

In his bedchamber, Richard frowns into the mirror. To keep the crown he's seized, he needs a better marriage. Once rid of Anne, he will marry Elizabeth, sister of the two little princes who still languish in the Tower.

The page enters, accompanied by a desperate, needy-looking gentleman by the name of Sir James Tyrrel. Richard gestures for the page to leave.

RICHARD   Dar'st thou resolve to kill a friend of mine?

TYRREL   Please you, but I had rather kill two enemies.

RICHARD   Why then thou hast it; two deep enemies. Tyrrel, I mean those bastards in the Tower.

TYRREL   I will dispatch it straight! (*He hastens away. No sooner has he left than Buckingham enters.*)

BUCKINGHAM   My lord, I have consider'd in my mind the late request that you did sound me in.

RICHARD   (*with an airy wave of his hand*) Well, let that rest.

BUCKINGHAM   My lord, I claim the gift, my due by promise, th' earldom of Hereford –

RICHARD   (*as if not hearing*) I do remember me, Henry the Sixth did prophesy that Richmond should be king, when Richmond was a little peevish boy.

BUCKINGHAM   My lord, your promise for the earldom!

RICHARD   I am not in the giving vein today. Thou troublest me; I am not in the vein. (*Richard moves away, leaving Buckingham red-faced and alone.*)

BUCKINGHAM   And is it thus? Repays he my deep service with such contempt?
Made I him king for this? O, let me think on Hastings, and be
gone!

*If Buckingham had proved a broken reed, Tyrrel was made of
sterner stuff. With the help of two sturdy assistants, he
smothers the two children while they sleep.*
*In the royal apartments, Richard, surrounded by servants,
attires himself splendidly in front of a mirror.*

RICHARD   The sons of Edward sleep in Abraham's bosom, and Anne my wife hath bid this world good night. Now, for I know that Richmond aims at young Elizabeth, my brother's daughter, and by that knot looks proudly on the crown – to her go I, a jolly thriving wooer. (*Richard hops but suddenly Catesby stands in his path.*)

RICHARD   (*with irritation*) Good or bad news, that thou com'st in so bluntly?

CATESBY   Bad news, my lord: Ely is fled to Richmond, and Buckingham, back'd with the hardy Welshmen, is in the field, and still his power increaseth.

RICHARD   (*clenching his fists*) Go, muster men. We must be brief, when traitors brave the field.

But the news goes from bad to worse.

MESSENGER   My lord, the army of great Buckingham is –

RICHARD   Out on you, owls! Nothing but songs of death? (*He strikes him. The messenger falls down.*) There, take thou that, till thou bring better news!

MESSENGER   (*getting up*) The news I have to tell your majesty is that by sudden flood and fall of water Buckingham's army is dispers'd and scatter'd, and he himself wander'd away alone.

RICHARD   I cry thee mercy; there is my purse to cure that blow of thine. (*He flings some money at him.*)

CATESBY   My liege, the Duke of Buckingham is taken: that is the best news. That the Earl of Richmond is with a mighty power landed at Milford is colder tidings, yet they must be told.

RICHARD   Away towards Salisbury! While we reason here, a royal battle might be won and lost!

Outside the palace, Richard is setting forth at the head of his army. Trumpets blaze, drums roar. On the bridge, he is confronted by two raging women: his mother, the Duchess of York, and the queen. The music ceases.

QUEEN   Tell me, thou villain-slave, where are my children?

DUCHESS   Thou toad, thou toad, where is thy brother Clarence?

At a sign from Richard, music strikes up, and the duchess' voiced is drowned. At another sign, it ceases.

RICHARD   Be patient and entreat me fair, and brief, good mother, for I am in haste.

DUCHESS   Art thou so hasty? I have stay'd for thee, God knows, in torment and in agony.

RICHARD   And came I not at last to comfort you?

DUCHESS   Thou cam'st on earth to make the earth my hell! Therefore take with thee my most grievous curse, which in the day of battle tire thee more than all the complete armour that thou wear'st! Bloody thou art, bloody will be thy end; shame serves thy life and doth thy death attend!

The two women turn and stalk away, their robes flapping like birds of ill-omen. Richard laughs and rides away.

Though he is beset by troubles, the hunchback king does not forget his friends. He gives orders for the Duke of Buckingham to be put to death. Like the good politician he is, he knows the importance of detail and when his camp is pitched on Bosworth field, he is everywhere spying out weaknesses. Now he is prepared for battle.

RICHARD   Here will I lie tonight —
           But where tomorrow? Well, all's one for that!

It is night. Richard is alone in his tent. The lamp flickers on the table and his armour lies on the floor, like a dead king. He remembers his mother's curse.

Richard goes to the entrance of his tent and speaks to his officers.

RICHARD   Stir with the lark tomorrow, gentle Norfolk.

NORFOLK   I warrant you, my lord.

RICHARD   (*to another officer*) Give me a bowl of wine. I have not that alacrity of spirit nor cheer of mind that I was wont to have. Leave me.

Richard is alone in his tent. He sits wearily down on his bed and drinks a glass of wine in one gulp. He puts the glass on the table and watches the light of the lamp. He sleeps. The lamp begins to burn blue. Strange, flimsy white wisps enter the tent. They gather round the sleeping king. Little by little, they assume more definite shapes. They are the ghosts of his victims. They go in circles above Richard, one by one coming closer to him. Richards stirs and tosses in his sleep.

GHOST OF
CLARENCE   Poor Clarence, by thy guile betray'd to death – tomorrow in the battle think on me.

ALL GHOSTS   Despair and die!

GHOST OF
HASTINGS   In a bloody battle end thy days! Think on Lord Hastings!

ALL GHOSTS   Despair and die!

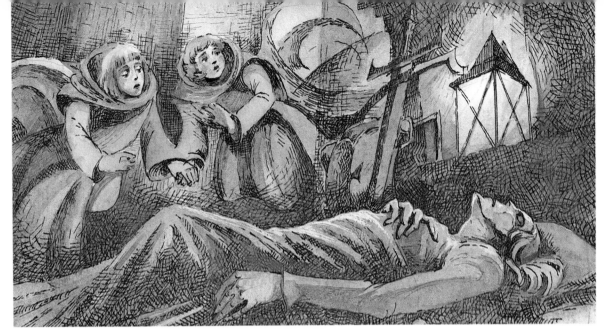

GHOSTS OF TWO LITTLE PRINCES	Dream on thy cousins smother'd in the Tower.
ALL GHOSTS	Despair and die!
GHOST OF ANNE	Richard, thy wife, that wretched Anne, thy wife. Tomorrow in the battle think on me.
ALL GHOSTS	Despair and die!
GHOST OF BUCKINGHAM	The first was I that help'd thee to the crown; the last was I that felt thy tyranny. O, in the battle think of Buckingham, and die in terror of thy guiltiness.

Richard awakes and looks around him in terror.

RICHARD   Soft, I did but dream. What do I fear? Myself? (*He sees his huge shadow on the wall of the tent and smiles at it.*) Richard loves Richard: that is, I and I. Is there a murderer here? (*He draws his dagger.*) No. Yes, I am. Then fly. What, from myself?

Richard pours wine into a goblet. His hands are shaking. He spills some wine, which spreads like a pool of blood over the table. He drinks the wine in one gulp.

RICHARD   Let not our babbling dreams affright our souls; conscience is but a word that cowards use, devis'd at first to keep the strong in awe. Our strong arms be our conscience, swords our law.

Richard is himself again.

On the hillside, in the early morning mist, Richard, on his great white horse, rides up and down before his troops. He looks up to the sky.

RICHARD   The sun will not be seen today. Not shine today? Why, what is that to me more than to Richmond?

He looks towards the place where Richmond's troops are waiting. Suddenly a sun-ray cuts through the clouds. Richmond's armour flares up in gold. He is ahead of his troops.

NORFOLK   (*riding up to Richard*) Arm, arm, my lord; the foe vaunts in the field!

RICHARD   Come, bustle, bustle! (*He addresses his troops.*) March on! Join bravely. Let us to it pell-mell, if not to Heaven, then hand in hand to hell! Fight, gentlemen of England! Fight, bold yeomen! Draw, archers, draw your arrows to the head. Advance, our standards. Set upon our foes!

He waves, and the advance begins, down the hillside towards the enemy. Richard's troops mingle with Richmond's troops in battle, Richard laying about him like a madman. At last, his horse is killed. He scrambles to his feet and fights on.

RICHARD   A horse! A horse! My kingdom for a horse!

Catesby rides by.

CATESBY   Withdraw, my lord. I'll help you to a horse.

RICHARD   Slave, I have set my life upon a cast, and I will stand the hazard
           of the die! I think there be six Richmonds in the field: five have
           I slain today instead of him!

           *He stumbles away, killing and killing. Suddenly he confronts
           the tall, golden figure of Richmond. He raises his sword. The
           air is full of whispers. He strikes out, but his sword is heavy.
           Richmond in a single blow cuts off Richard's head.*
               *The crown is brought to Richmond. He puts it on and all
           kneel before him.*

RICHMOND   (*staring around the battlefield that is littered with the dead*)
           England hath long been mad and scarr'd herself: the brother
           blindly shed the brother's blood; the father rashly slaughter'd
           his own son; the son, compell'd, been butcher to the sire. All
           this divided York and Lancaster – O, now let Richmond and
           Elizabeth, the true succeeders of each royal house, by God's
           fair ordinance conjoin together! Now civil wounds are stopp'd,
           peace lives again. That she may long live here, God say amen!

           The curtain falls.

THE TAMING OF THE SHREW

Written, probably, in 1592, when the playwright was twenty-eight, *The Taming of the Shrew* is one of Shakespeare's earliest comedies. It is also one of his funniest. For four hundred years, the antics of Kate and Petruchio, as they trade insults, blows and kisses on their stormy way from courtship to marriage to perfect love and understanding, have filled the world's theatres with laughter and delight. But there is more to the play than a knockabout, boisterous battle of the sexes. It is a play about change, about transformation, about the magic of the theatre itself, when, at one moment, we are watching a group of people in strange costume strutting about on bare boards, and the next, we are in a street in sunny Padua, watching old Baptista Minola, trying to marry off his turbulent daughter Kate, to whoever is brave enough to take her ...

LEON GARFIELD

The curtain rises on the outside of a country inn. Christopher Sly, the tinker, is drunk. Indeed, he is not often sober; and the hostess of the inn where he does his drinking has had enough of him.

HOSTESS'S VOICE   A pair of stocks, you rogue!

The door bursts open and out staggers Sly. He slides down the tethering post, and finishes up on the ground. He sleeps, his mouth wide open – a picture of drunken brutishness. There is a winding of horns. Enter a lord from hunting, with his train. He sees the recumbent Sly.

LORD   Grim death, how foul and loathsome is thy visage. (*Sly stirs, hiccups and snores.*)

SLY   The Slys are no rogues.

The lord starts back. He frowns, then smiles, as a thought strikes him. He beckons his servants about him.

LORD   (*confidentially*) Sirs, I will practise on this drunken man.

The drunken Sly is transported to the lord's mansion where he is wrapped in new clothes, rings put upon his fingers, a banquet laid for him, and servants ordered to wait upon him as if he was indeed the lord of the mansion.

 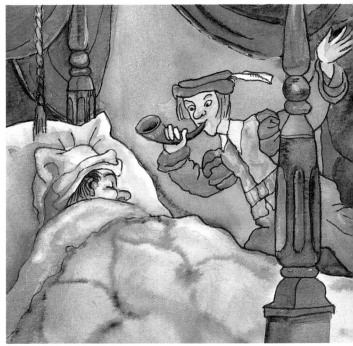

SLY   (*waking*) For God's sake, a pot of small ale!

1ST SERVANT   Your honour –

2ND SERVANT   Your lordship –

SLY   Call me not 'honour', nor 'lordship'. Am I not Christopher Sly, old Sly's son of Burton Heath?

LORD   Thou art a lord and nothing but a lord.

2ND SERVANT   These fifteen years you have been in a dream.

SLY   These fifteen years! By my fay, a goodly nap! Upon my life, I am a lord indeed!

1ST SERVANT   Your doctors thought it good you hear a play and frame your mind to mirth and merriment.

SLY   Well, we'll see it.

Sly is led from his bed to a great hall, at the farthest end of which is a curtained stage. The performance is about to begin.

The curtain rises on a street in Padua. Enter Baptista with his two daughters, Katerina and Bianca, together with Bianca's suitors, young Hortensio and old Gremio.

BAPTISTA   Gentlemen, importune me no farther for how I firmly am resolved you know – that is, not to bestow my youngest daughter before I have a husband for the elder. If either of you both love Katerina, leave shall you have to court her at your pleasure.

While her father speaks, Katerina – Kate – a wild and fearsome lass, is doing her best, by means of surreptitious pinches, kicks and tweakings of her fair plaits, to make her angel sister Bianca's life a misery.

GREMIO   To cart her rather! She's too rough for me!

KATE   (*to Baptista*) I pray you, sir, is it your will to make a stale of me amongst these mates?

HORTENSIO   'Mates', maid? No mates for you unless you were of gentler, milder mould. (*Kate threatens him with her fist. Hortensio backs away.*) From all such devils, good Lord deliver us!

GREMIO   (*skipping behind Hortensio*) And me too, good Lord!

BAPTISTA   Bianca, get you in. (*She looks downcast.*) And let it not displease thee, good Bianca, for I will love thee ne'er the less, my girl.

KATE   (*pulling Bianca's hair*) A pretty peat!

BIANCA   Sister, content you in my discontent. Sir, to your pleasure I humbly subscribe. (*She goes towards the door of her house, picking up a pretty guitar hung with ribbons and trailing it behind her.*)

GREMIO   Why, will you mew her up, Signor Baptista, for this fiend of hell?

As she dawdles, we see Lucentio, a young gallant, peering round a pillar at Bianca – obviously much attracted!

BAPTISTA   Gentlemen, content ye. I am resolved. (*Bianca goes into the house. Baptista follows, then pauses and turns to Kate.*) Katerina, you may stay. (*He goes in.*)

KATE   Why, and I trust I may go too, may I not? Ha!

She flounces into the house and slams the door violently. The gentlemen look at one another. Comes another loud bang as another door is slammed. They jump, and Lucentio does too.

It was a wretched state of affairs! No matter the suitors' sighs, old Baptista would never give his consent to the marriage of the fair Bianca until a husband was found for Katerina. And no consent, no dowry.

The scene changes to Petruchio, a gentleman from Verona, on horseback, knocking at Hortensio's window. Hortensio greets him enthusiastically.

HORTENSIO   My good friend Petruchio! What happy gale blows you to Padua here from old Verona?

PETRUCHIO   Such wind as scatters young men through the world. Signor Hortensio, I come to wive it wealthily in Padua; if weathily, then happily in Padua.

HORTENSIO   (*thoughtfully*) I can, Petruchio, help thee to a wife with wealth enough, and young, and beauteous, brought up as best becomes a gentlewoman. Her only fault – and that is faults enough – is that she is intolerable curst, and shrewd and froward. I would not wed her for a mine of gold!

PETRUCHIO   Hortensio, peace. Thou know'st not gold's effect. I will not sleep, Hortensio, till I see her . . .

Outside Baptista's house. Kate emerges, followed by a weeping Bianca, her hands tied.

BIANCA   Good sister, wrong me not, nor wrong yourself, to make a bondmaid and a slave of me.

Kate, detecting spite in the last remark, drags Bianca to the fountain. Baptista appears.

BAPTISTA   Why, how now dame, whence grows this insolence? Poor girl, she weeps. (*He unties her hands and turns to Kate.*) For shame, thou hilding of a devilish spirit, why dost thou wrong her that did ne'er wrong thee? Bianca, get thee in.

Bianca goes in.

KATE   Nay, now I see she is your treasure, she must have a husband, I must dance barefoot on her wedding day! Talk not to me, I will go sit and weep, till I can find occasion for revenge! (*She rushes into the house, with the inevitable slamming of the door.*)

BAPTISTA   Was ever gentleman thus grieved as I? But who comes here?

Enter Petruchio, who greets Baptista courteously.

PETRUCHIO I am a gentleman of Verona, sir. Petruchio is my name. Pray have you not a daughter called Katerina, fair and virtuous?

BAPTISTA I have a daughter, sir, called Katerina.

PETRUCHIO Signor Baptista, my business asketh haste, and every day I cannot come to woo. Then tell me, if I get your daughter's love, what dowry shall I have with her to wife?

BAPTISTA *(looking startled)* After my death the one half of my lands, and in possession twenty thousand crowns.

PETRUCHIO *(nodding approvingly)* Let covenants be therefore drawn between us.

BAPTISTA *(suddenly overcome with conscience)* Ay, where the special thing is well obtained, that is, her love; for that is all in all.

PETRUCHIO Why, that is nothing; for I tell you, father, I am as peremptory as she proud-minded, and when two raging fires meet together they do consume the thing that feeds their fury.

BAPTISTA Well mayst thou woo, and happy be thy speed! Be thou armed for some unhappy words. Shall I send my daughter Kate to you?

PETRUCHIO I pray you do, I'll attend her here . . . (*Baptista, unable to believe his good fortune, hastens within. Petruchio is alone.*)

Kate appears. She eyes Petruchio curiously, as he does her. It is plain that an instant interest has been kindled between them, and they regard one another as worthy adversaries.

PETRUCHIO   Good morrow, Kate – for that's your name, I hear.

KATE   Well have you heard, but something hard of hearing; they call me Katherine that do talk of me.

PETRUCHIO   You lie, in faith, for you are called plain Kate, and bonny Kate, and sometimes Kate the curst. But Kate, the prettiest Kate in Christendom, hearing thy mildness praised in every town, thy virtues spoke of, and thy beauty sounded, myself am moved to woo thee for a wife!

KATE   'Moved', in good time! Let him that moved you hither remove you hence!

PETRUCHIO   Come, come, you wasp, i' faith, you are too angry.

KATE   If I be waspish, best beware my sting!

PETRUCHIO   My remedy then is to pluck it out!

KATE   Ay, if the fool could find it where it lies.

PETRUCHIO   Who knows not where a wasp does wear his sting? In his tail. (*He puts his hand on her bottom. She breaks loose.*)

KATE   And so farewell! (*She turns to go.*)

PETRUCHIO   Nay, come again. Good Kate, I am a gentleman –

KATE   That I'll try! (*She strikes him.*)

PETRUCHIO   I swear I'll cuff you if you strike again!

KATE   If you strike me you are no gentleman. (*They struggle.*)

PETRUCHIO   In sooth, you scape not so!

KATE   Let me go!

PETRUCHIO   (*releasing her so suddenly that she falls*) Why does the world report that Kate doth limp? O sland'rous world! Kate like the hazel twig is straight and slender. O let me see thee walk. Thou dost not halt.

KATE   Go, fool.

PETRUCHIO   Am I not wise?

KATE   Yes, keep you warm.

PETRUCHIO   Marry, so I mean, sweet Katherine, in thy bed. Now, Kate, I am a husband for your turn. For I am he am born to tame you, Kate, and bring you from a wild Kate to a Kate conformable as other household Kates.

It is apparent that Kate, in spite of herself, is much attracted to Petruchio, and his praise of her beauty does not go unnoticed. Old Baptista arrives.

BAPTISTA   Now, Signor Petruchio, how speed you with my daughter?

PETRUCHIO   How but well, sir? We have 'greed so well together that upon Sunday is the wedding day!

KATE   I'll see thee hanged on Sunday first.

Petruchio laughs, and confides to Baptista, unheard by Kate.

PETRUCHIO   'Tis bargained 'twixt us twain, being alone, that she shall still be curst in company. I tell you 'tis incredible to believe how much she loves me! O, the kindest Kate! She hung about my neck, and kiss on kiss she vied so fast, that in a twink she won me to her love!

BAPTISTA   I know not what to say, but give me your hands. God send you joy; Petruchio, 'tis a match.

PETRUCHIO   Provide the feast, father, and bid the guests: I will to Venice; Sunday comes apace. We will have rings, and things, and fine array. And kiss me, Kate, we will be married o' Sunday!

Kate glares at Petruchio, then at her father, then at Petruchio again. She kisses him; then, wiping the kiss off her lips, rushes into the house, slamming the door behind her. Baptista looks dismayed; but Petruchio wags a finger as if to say, 'I told you so', and departs. Baptista sighs with relief.

Invitations are dispatched and Kate's wedding-gown is prepared. By Sunday, the bride is ready, and everyone awaits the coming of the bridegroom. They wait, and they wait, and they wait.

KATE   I told you, I, he was a frantic fool. Now must the world point at poor Katherine and say, 'Lo, there is mad Petruchio's wife, if it would please him come and marry her!' (*She rushes out weeping in fury and a sense of betrayal.*)

BAPTISTA   Go, girl, I cannot blame thee now to weep, for such an injury would vex a saint.

A servant enters, breathless.

SERVANT   Master, master, news, and such news as you never heard of!

BAPTISTA   Is he come?

For answer, the servant points, and Petruchio, accompanied by his servant, appears. He is dressed in 'a new hat and an old jerkin; a pair of old breeches thrice turned; a pair of boots that have been candle-cases, one buckled, another laced; an old rusty sword . . .' In short, a very scarecrow. He dismounts. The guests watch, amazed.

PETRUCHIO   *(ignoring the stares)* Where is Kate? The morning wears, 'tis time we were in church.

BAPTISTA   But thus I trust you will not marry her.

PETRUCHIO   Good sooth, even thus. To me she's married, not unto my clothes. But what a fool am I to chat with you, when I should bid good morrow to my bride, and seal the title with a lovely kiss! *(He departs.)*

All stare at one another appalled.

In Baptista's house, the wedding guests await the arrival of the happy couple. Petruchio enters with his tousled bride.

PETRUCHIO Gentlemen and friends, I thank you for your pains. I know you think to dine with me today, but so it is, my haste doth call me hence.

BAPTISTA Is't possible you will away tonight?

PETRUCHIO I must away before night come.

GREMIO Let me entreat you to stay 'til after dinner.

PETRUCHIO It cannot be.

KATE Let me entreat you. Now if you love me, stay.

PETRUCHIO Grumio, my horse!

KATE Nay then, do what thou canst, I will not go today, no, nor tomorrow, not till I please myself. Gentlemen, forward to the bridal dinner. I see a woman may be made a fool if she had not a spirit to resist.

PETRUCHIO They shall go forward, Kate, at thy command. — Obey the bride, you that attend on her. Go to the feast, and carouse full measure to her maidenhead. But for my bonny Kate, she must with me. I will be master of what is mine own.

Kate shows every sign of defiance and seeks support from her father and the guests. It is not forthcoming. At length, Petruchio seizes her about the waist, and, with fiercely drawn sword, rushes away with her, followed by his servant, Grumio. The guests crowd after them.

Outside, Kate, Petruchio and Grumio gallop away on three horses. Inside, all is cheerfulness. Bianca is queening it among her admirers.

LUCENTIO   Mistress, what is your opinion of your sister?

BIANCA   That being mad herself, she's madly mated!

The three riders in a wet and windy landscape. Kate's horse stumbles and she tumbles down. The horse bolts. Petruchio hoists Kate up onto his own horse, and away they ride, he behind, she in front, muddy and furious.

At last, they arrive at Petruchio's house in Verona where the servants are making ready for the arrival of the master and his bride.

PETRUCHIO   Where be these knaves? What, no man at door to hold my stirrup nor to take my horse?

ALL SERVANTS Here sir, here sir, here sir!

While Kate is learning one lesson, her sister, the fair Bianca, is learning another . . .

In Baptista's house, Bianca is closeted with her new suitor, Lucentio, a rich young man from Pisa, who cunningly disguised as a schoolmaster has outbid his rivals and won Bianca's heart.

BIANCA	What, master, read you?
LUCENTIO	The Art to Love.
BIANCA	And may you prove, sir, master of your art!
LUCENTIO	While you, sweet dear, prove mistress of my heart.

He removes his whiskers and kisses her. Meanwhile, Hortensio and Gremio give up their hopes for Bianca's love: Gremio retires to his moneybags, and Hortensio decides to marry a rich widow. But first he calls at his friend Petruchio's house.

He finds Kate seated at a table. Petruchio and Hortensio enter with a dish of meat.

HORTENSIO	Mistress, what cheer?
KATE	Faith, as cold as can be.
PETRUCHIO	Pluck up thy spirits! Here, love, thou seest how diligent I am to dress thy meat myself. What, not a word? Nay then, thou lov'st it not. Here, take away this dish.

A servant comes forward.

KATE	I pray you let it stand.
PETRUCHIO	The poorest service is repaid with thanks, and so shall mine before you touch the meat.
KATE	I thank you, sir.
PETRUCHIO	Kate, eat apace. And now, my honey love, we will return unto thy father's house, and revel it as bravely as the best, with silken coats and caps, and golden rings – what, hast thou dined? (*He takes away her unfinished plate.*) The tailor stays thy leisure.

The tailor enters.

TAILOR	Here is the cap your worship did bespeak.
PETRUCHIO	Why, 'tis a cockle or a walnut shell. A baby's cap. Come, let me have a bigger.
KATE	I'll have no bigger. Gentlewomen wear such caps as these.
PETRUCHIO	When you are gentle, you shall have one too, and not till then.
HORTENSIO	That will not be in haste!
PETRUCHIO	Thy gown? Come, tailor, let us see it. (*The tailor displays the gown.*) What's this? A sleeve? Carved like an apple tart? Here's snip and nip, and cut and slish and slash! (*The tailor retreats, baffled.*)
HORTENSIO	(*aside*) I see she's like to have neither cap nor gown.
PETRUCHIO	I'll none of it! (*To the tailor*) Away, thou rag, thou quantity, thou remnant! (*He rips the dress. Kate is in despair.*)
KATE	I never saw a better-fashioned gown.

Petruchio mutters to Hortensio as tailor retreats.

PETRUCHIO	Hortensio, say thou wilt see the tailor paid. Well, come my Kate, we will unto your father's, even in these honest mean habiliments. Our purses shall be proud, our garments poor, for 'tis the mind that makes the body rich. Let's see, I think 'tis now some seven o'clock, and well we may come there by dinner-time.
KATE	I dare assure you, sir, 'tis almost two.
PETRUCHIO	It shall be what o'clock I say it is.
HORTENSIO	(*aside*) Why, so this gallant will command the sun!

The scene changes to Petruchio, Kate and Hortensio on horseback.

PETRUCHIO	Come on, a God's name, once more towards our father's. Good Lord, how bright and goodly shines the moon!

KATE   The moon? The sun! It is not moonlight now.

PETRUCHIO   I say it is the moon that shines so bright.

KATE   I know it is the sun that shines so bright.

PETRUCHIO   (*stopping*) Evermore crossed and crossed, nothing but crossed.

KATE   Forward, I pray, and be it moon or sun, or what you please –

PETRUCHIO   I say it is the moon.

KATE   I know it is the moon.

PETRUCHIO   Nay, then you lie. It is the blessed sun.

KATE   Then God be blessed, it is the blessed sun, but sun it is not, when you say it is not, and the moon changes even as your mind; what you shall have it named, even that it is, and so it shall be so for Katherine.

*And so they come to Padua. Hortensio marries his rich widow,
and Bianca marries her lover Lucentio. And afterwards, there
is a great banquet.*

BAPTISTA   (*becoming maudlin*) Now, in good sadness, son Petruchio, I
think thou hast the veriest shrew of all.

PETRUCHIO   Well, I say no. And therefore, for assurance, let's each one send
unto his wife, and he whose wife is most obedient, shall win
the wager which we will propose.

HORTENSIO   Content. What's the wager?

LUCENTIO   Twenty crowns.

PETRUCHIO   Twenty crowns? I'll venture so much of my hawk or hound,
            but twenty times so much upon my wife!

LUCENTIO   A hundred then.

PETRUCHIO   A match! 'Tis done.

HORTENSIO   Who shall begin?

LUCENTIO   That will I. (*To servant*) Go, bid your mistress come to me.

*The servant leaves, watched contentedly by Lucentio and
Baptista. Soon he returns.*

LUCENTIO   How now, what news?

SERVANT   Sir, my mistress sends you word that she is busy, and she
            cannot come.

PETRUCHIO   How? 'She's busy, and she cannot come'? Is that an answer?

GREMIO   Pray God, sir, your wife send you not a worse!

HORTENSIO   (*to servant*) Go and entreat my wife to come to me forthwith.
            (*The servant leaves the room.*)

PETRUCHIO   O ho, entreat her! Nay, then she needs must come!

HORTENSIO   I am afraid, sir, do what you can, yours will not be entreated.
            (*The servant returns.*) Now, where's my wife?

SERVANT   She will not come; she bids you come to her.

PETRUCHIO   Worse and worse; 'She will not come'! O vile, intolerable, not to be endured. (*To* Grumio, *his servant*) Go to your mistress, say I command her to come to me. (*Grumio departs.*)

HORTENSIO   I know her answer.

PETRUCHIO   What?

HORTENSIO   She will not.

Kate enters charmingly.

KATE   What is your will, sir, that you send for me?

PETRUCHIO   Where is your sister, and Hortensio's wife?

KATE   They sit conferring by the parlour fire.

PETRUCHIO   Away, I say, and bring them hither straight!

Kate leaves.

LUCENTIO   Here is a wonder, if you talk of wonder!

HORTENSIO   And so it is. I wonder what it bodes.

PETRUCHIO   Marry, peace it bodes, and love, and quiet life.

BAPTISTA   Now fair befall thee, good Petruchio! The wager thou hast won, and I will add unto their losses twenty thousand crowns, another dowry to another daughter, for she is changed, as she had never been!

PETRUCHIO   Nay, I will win my wager better yet. (*Kate enters, propelling the unwilling Bianca, now a grim and furious angel, and the widow.*) Katherine, that cap of yours becomes you not. Off with that bauble! (*Kate smiles, takes off the cap and treads on it.*)

WIDOW   Lord, let me never have cause to sigh till I be brought to such a silly pass!

BIANCA   Fie, what a foolish duty call you this?

LUCENTIO   I wish your duty were as foolish too! The wisdom of your duty, fair Bianca, hath cost me a hundred crowns since supper-time.

BIANCA   The more fool you for laying on my duty!

PETRUCHIO   Katherine, I charge thee tell these headstrong women what duty they do owe their lords and husbands.

WIDOW   She shall not!

KATE   (*with exaggeration, Petruchio finding it hard to restrain himself from laughing at their mutual joke*) Fie, fie, unknit that threatening unkind brow. It blots thy beauty. A woman moved is like a fountain troubled, muddy, ill-seeming, thick, bereft of beauty. Thy husband is thy lord, thy life, thy keeper – one that cares for thee; and for thy maintenance, commits his body to painful labour both by sea and land, whilst thou liest warm at home, secure and safe, and craves no other tribute at thy hands but love, fair looks, and true obedience – too little payment for so great a debt.

Kate lays her hands under her husband's feet with a dramatic flourish and smiles triumphantly up at him. He looks adoringly at her.

PETRUCHIO   Why, there's a wench! Come on, and kiss me, Kate! (*She does so. He turns to Lucentio.*) 'Twas I won the wager, and being a winner, God give you good night! (*They leave together, fondly entwined.*)

The play is over and Christopher Sly is fast asleep. The lord and his companions smile. The tinker's dream must end where it began.

    Sly is carried back to the ale-house where he had been found and left propped against the tethering-post. He awakes.

SLY   Sim, gi's some more wine. What's all the players gone? (*He surveys his own wretched attire, and sadly shakes his head.*) Am I not a lord? (*He sighs, then he smiles.*) I have had the bravest dream. I know now how to tame a shrew.

He rises uncertainly, and totters into the ale-house with some determination. A moment latter, he comes out, a good deal more rapidly than he went in, followed by a hail of household utensils.

HOSTESS'S VOICE   A pair of stocks, you rogue!

The curtain falls.

OTHELLO

This is the story of a great general, a man in whom the state of Venice has put all its trust, a black man of immense dignity and splendour who is brought to madness, murder and suicide by the skilful lies of the lieutenant he trusts and calls 'honest Iago'. "Will you, I pray," asks the tragically bewildered Othello, when Iago's villainy is discovered, "demand that demi-devil why he hath thus ensnared my soul and body?" "Demand me nothing;" answers Iago, "what you know, you know; from this time forth I never will speak word."

It is a marvellous, terrifying play, in which Shakespeare, at the very height of his powers, has created, in Iago, the most devilish villain in all drama: most devilish because, although he gives reasons for his hatred of Othello, they are too small for the monstrousness of his revenge.

LEON GARFIELD

The curtain rises on a chapel. Othello the Moor, commander of all the forces of Venice, is to marry Desdemona. But it is a wedding that causes more rage than joy. Not only to Desdemona's father, Brabantio, but to Iago, Othello's ensign.

IAGO   (*watching Desdemona and Othello*) I do hate him as I hate hell's pains. (*They kiss.*) O, you are well-tuned now! But I'll set down the pegs that make this music, as honest as I am.

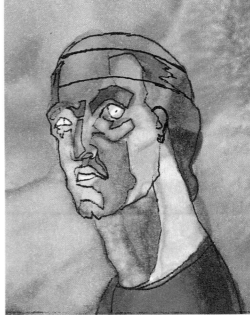

Iago rushes through the dim and torchlit streets of Venice. He reaches Brabantio's house and bangs on the door.

IAGO   Signior Brabantio, ho! Awake!

BRABANTIO   What is the matter there?

IAGO   Look to your house, your daughter! Even now, very now, an old black ram is tupping your white ewe! Your daughter and the Moor are now making the beast with two backs!

Brabantio searches his house and discovers his daughter gone. With armed servants, he rushes through the streets to Othello's lodging and thunders on the door.

BRABANTIO   Who would be a father?

OTHELLO   Keep up your bright swords for the dew will rust them!

BRABANTIO   O thou foul thief! Where hast thou stowed my daughter?

OTHELLO   Where will you that I go and answer to this charge?

In the council chamber, Brabantio throws himself before the duke and accuses Othello who stands by with Iago.

BRABANTIO   Oh, my daughter is abused, stolen from me and corrupted by witchcraft and medicines!

DUKE   (*to Othello*)What can you say to this?

OTHELLO   That I have ta'en away this old man's daughter, it is most true. True I have married her. This only is the witchcraft I have used . . . Her father loved me, oft invited me, still questioned me the story of my life. She loved me for the dangers I had passed, and I loved her, that she did pity them.

The duke and his fellow dignitaries listen entranced to Othello's adventures.

DUKE   I think this tale would win my daughter too. Valiant Othello, we must straight employ you against the general enemy. You must hence tonight.

At the crowded quayside, Venetian ships make ready to set sail for Cyprus. Brabantio shouts to Othello who is already aboard.

BRABANTIO   Look to her, Moor, if thou hast eyes to see: she has deceived her father and may thee! (*He points to another ship on which Desdemona stands.*)

OTHELLO   My life upon her faith!

He waves to Desdemona, who waves back, with a strawberry-spotted handkerchief. Iago watches Othello and salutes him. Othello cordially returns the gesture. Roderigo, an elegant young gallant, sidles up beside Iago, gazing in a love-sick way at Desdemona.

IAGO   (*nudging Roderigo suggestively*) I have told thee often, I hate the Moor. If thou canst cuckold him, thou dost thyself a pleasure, and me a sport.

Roderigo smiles hopefully, and slips some money into Iago's ready hand. He departs.

The fleet sets sail but a storm springs up and before long drives the vessels apart. The first ship to reach Cyprus carries Cassio, a young man Othello has promoted over Iago's head to be his lieutenant; then comes a vessel carrying Iago and his wife Emilia, lady-in-waiting to Othello's bride.

CASSIO   (*greeting Desdemona as she disembarks*) O behold, the riches
of the ship is come ashore! Hail to thee, lady!

*He kneels and kisses his fingers in gallant admiration of
Desdemona. She extends her hand, which Cassio takes fondly,
and rises, kissing her hand as he does so.*

IAGO   (*aside*) Very good, well kissed, an excellent courtesy. With as
little a web as this will I ensnare as great a fly as Cassio.

DESDEMONA   What tidings can you tell me of my lord?

CASSIO   He is not yet –

*He is interrupted by a cry of 'A sail, A sail!' Desdemona looks
eagerly to sea. Cassio kisses Emilia.*

IAGO   Sir, would she give you so much of her lips as of her tongue she
oft bestows on me, you'd have enough.

DESDEMONA   Alas, she has no speech!

CASSIO   Lo, where he comes.

Othello appears and greets Desdemona.

OTHELLO   O, my fair warrior!

DESDEMONA   My dear Othello!

They embrace, as Iago looks on. Then all depart, except for Iago and Roderigo. Iago beckons to Roderigo who draws close.

IAGO   Lieutenant Cassio tonight watches on the court of guard. First, I must tell thee this: Desdemona is directly in love with him.

RODERIGO   I cannot believe that in her; she's full of most blest condition!

IAGO   Blest pudding! Didst thou not see her paddle with the palm of his hand?

RODERIGO   Well?

IAGO   Do you find some occasion to anger Cassio. He's rash, and haply may strike at you. So shall you have a shorter journey to your desires . . .

It is night. In a courtyard, Cassio and a group of officers are seated round a table on which there are bottles of wine. Iago enters.

CASSIO   Welcome, Iago; we must to the watch.

IAGO   Not this hour, lieutenant; I have a stoup of wine –

He produces a bottle, and offers it to Cassio.

CASSIO   Not tonight, good Iago; I have very poor and unhappy brains for drinking.

IAGO   But one cup – (*Cassio protests and turns away. The others try to tempt him.*) If I can fasten but one cup upon him, he'll be as full of quarrel and offence as my young mistress' dog. (*Iago sees that Cassio still resists and approaches him, the bottle in hand.*) Some wine, ho! (*He seizes hold of Cassio affectionately. Music strikes up. Iago sings.*)

> And let me the cannikin clink, clink.
> And let me the cannikin clink;
> A soldier's a man,
> O, man's life's but a span,
> Why then, let a soldier drink!
> Why then, let a soldier drink!

Some wine . . . Cassio!

During the song, Iago begins to whirl Cassio round and round, laughingly forcing wine down his throat. The others join in. The dance becomes wild and whirling. At the height of it, Roderigo appears and taunts Cassio. Madly, drunkenly, Cassio draws his sword.

CASSIO   Villain! Villain, knave!

Roderigo flees. Officers try to restrain Cassio, but he is incensed. He fights and wounds Montano. In the midst of the uproar, Othello enters.

OTHELLO   Hold for your lives! What is the matter, masters? Who began this? (*They all fall back, and leave the wretched, drunken Cassio swaying, with his bloody sword in his hand. Othello looks at him sorrowfully.*) Cassio, I love thee, but never more be officer of mine.

All depart. Cassio is left alone, weeping with shame. Iago insinuates himself beside him.

IAGO   What, are you hurt, lieutenant?

CASSIO   Ay, past all surgery. O, I have lost the immortal part of myself. My reputation, Iago, my reputation!

IAGO   As I am an honest man, I thought you had received some bodily wound.

CASSIO Drunk! And speak like a parrot! O God.

IAGO Come, come, I'll tell you what you shall do. Our general's wife is now the general. Confess yourself freely to her, importune her – she'll help to put you in your place again.

CASSIO You advise me well. I will beseech the virtuous Desdemona to undertake for me. Good night, honest Iago.

Iago smiles after him.

IAGO For whiles this honest fool plies Desdemona to repair his fortunes, and she for him pleads strongly to the Moor, I'll pour this pestilence into his ear: that she repeals him for her body's lust. So will I turn her virtue into pitch, and out of her own goodness make the net that shall enmesh them all!

Next morning, Cassio takes Iago's advice. He approaches Desdemona in the palace garden and begs her to plead his cause with Othello.

DESDEMONA Be thou assured, good Cassio, I will do all my abilities in thy behalf. (*Cassio, ever the gentleman, fervently kisses her hand. She laughs.*) Therefore be merry, Cassio –

EMILIA Madam, here comes my lord!

CASSIO (*hastily*) Madam, I'll take my leave.

*He hastens away as Othello appears, accompanied by Iago.
Iago glares at the retreating Cassio.*

IAGO   Ha! I like not that.

OTHELLO   What dost thou say?

IAGO   Nothing my lord.

OTHELLO   Was not that Cassio that parted from my wife?

IAGO   Cassio, my lord? No, sure I cannot think it, that he would steal
            away so guilty-like, seeing you coming.

OTHELLO   I do believe 'twas he. Is he not honest?

IAGO   My lord, for aught I know.

*Othello stares at Iago, who shakes his head, looking at
Desdemona.*

OTHELLO   I think so too.

IAGO   Why, then I think Cassio's an honest man.

OTHELLO   I know thou art full of honesty, and weigh'st thy words. Thou
            dost mean something . . .

IAGO   Oh, beware jealousy, my lord! It is the green-eyed monster.

OTHELLO   Farewell, if more thou dost perceive, let me know more. (*Iago leaves. Othello gazes towards Desdemona.*) Excellent wretch! Perdition catch my soul but I do love thee; and when I love thee not, chaos is come again!

DESDEMONA   Good love, call him back.

OTHELLO   Who is't you mean?

DESDEMONA   Why, your lieutenant, Cassio.

OTHELLO   Not now, sweet Desdemona, some other time.

DESDEMONA   Shall't be tonight at supper?

OTHELLO   No, not tonight.

DESDEMONA   Why then, tomorrow night –

OTHELLO   I do beseech thee, to leave me but a little by myself.

DESDEMONA   Are you not well?

OTHELLO   I have a pain upon my forehead here.

DESDEMONA Let me but bind your head, within this hour it will be well again.

OTHELLO Your napkin is too little. (*He pushes the handkerchief aside and she drops it.*) Let it alone.

Emilia, left behind, picks up the handkerchief.

EMILIA This was her first remembrance from the Moor. My wayward husband hath a hundred times wooed me to steal it; but she so loves the token —

Iago enters.

IAGO What do you here alone?

EMILIA I have a thing for you. What will you give me now for that same handkerchief?

IAGO A good wench! Give it to me. (*He snatches it.*) I will in Cassio's lodging lose this napkin and let him find it. Trifles light as air are to the jealous confirmations strong as proofs of holy writ. This may do something. The Moor already changes with my poison . . .

As he speaks, Othello approaches. His countenance is tormented as his fearful thoughts present him, over and over again, with the vision of Cassio kissing his wife's hand, until the kiss becomes lascivious.

IAGO Look where he comes! Not poppy nor mandragora, nor all the drowsy syrups of the world, shall ever medicine thee to that sweet sleep which thou owed'st yesterday.

OTHELLO (*seizing Iago by the throat*) Villain, be sure thou prove my love a whore! Or woe upon thy life!

IAGO (*freeing himself*) O grace! O heaven defend me! Take note, take note, O world! To be direct and honest is not safe.

He retreats.

OTHELLO Nay, stay; give me a living reason, that she's disloyal.

IAGO I do not like the office; but I will go on. I lay with Cassio lately. In sleep, I heard him say, 'Sweet Desdemona, let us be wary, let us hide our loves'.

OTHELLO O monstrous, monstrous!

IAGO   Nay, this was but his dream –

OTHELLO   I'll tear her all to pieces!

IAGO   Nay, yet be wise; she may be honest yet. Have you not seen a handkerchief spotted with strawberries in your wife's hand?

OTHELLO   I gave her such a one; 'twas my first gift.

IAGO   I know not that; but such a handkerchief – I am sure it was your wife's – did I today see Cassio wipe his beard with.

OTHELLO   O blood, Iago, blood! Within these three days let me hear thee say that Cassio's not alive.

IAGO   My friend is dead: 'tis done as you request. But let her live.

OTHELLO   Damn her, lewd minx! Come, go with me apart. Now art thou my lieutenant.

IAGO   I am your own for ever.

In another part of the garden, Desdemona searches for the lost handkerchief. Emilia is with her.

DESDEMONA   Where should I lose that handkerchief, Emilia?

EMILIA   I know not, madam.

Othello enters.

DESDEMONA	How is't with you, my lord?
OTHELLO	I have a salt and sorry rheum offends me; lend me thy handkerchief.
DESDEMONA	Here, my lord.
OTHELLO	That which I gave you.
DESDEMONA	I have it not about me.
OTHELLO	That's a fault. That handkerchief did an Egyptian to my mother give. She told her, while she kept it, 'twould subdue my father entirely to her love; but if she lost it or made a gift of it, my father's eye should hold her loathly . . .
DESDEMONA	Then would to God that I had never seen't!
OTHELLO	Is't lost? Is't gone?

DESDEMONA	Heaven bless us! This is a trick to put me from my suit. Pray you let Cassio be received again.
OTHELLO	Fetch me that handkerchief.
DESDEMONA	I pray, talk me of Cassio.
OTHELLO	The handkerchief!

He rushes away like a madman. But the handkerchief has gone. Iago has put it in Cassio's lodging and Cassio, finding it and liking it, has given it to Bianca, his mistress, to copy.

Still searching for the handkerchief, Desdemona and Emilia leave the garden and presently Iago and Othello enter together. Othello leans almost pathetically, towards his new lieutenant. He is sweating and seems unwell.

OTHELLO	What hath he said?
IAGO	Faith, that he did — I know not what he did.
OTHELLO	But, what?
IAGO	Lie —

OTHELLO   With her?

IAGO   With her, on her, what you will.

OTHELLO   Lie with her? Lie on her? Handkerchief – confessions –
handkerchief! Is't possible? O devil!

*During the above wild outburst. Othello is overwhelmed by
hateful fancies, which finally dissolve into a red oblivion, like
the fires of hell. Gradually the fragmented images solidify into
Iago's face, looking down, much concerned.*

IAGO   How is it, general? Whilst you were here, mad with your grief,
Cassio came hither. I shifted him away; bade him anon return
and here speak with me. Do but encave yourself, for I will
make him tell the tale anew, where, how, how oft, how long
ago, and when he has and is again to cope your wife. Will you
withdraw?

*Othello, helplessly in the power of Iago, nods and hides
himself behind a trellis, like a netted beast. Cassio approaches.*

IAGO   (*to himself*) Now will I question Cassio of Bianca. As he shall
smile, Othello shall go mad.

Iago, with the skill of a dancer, leads Cassio, whispering in his ear, close to the trellis behind which Othello listens.

IAGO   (*to Cassio, aloud*) I never knew a woman love man so.

CASSIO   (*laughing*) Alas, poor rogue! I think i' faith she loves me. She hangs and lolls and weeps upon me, so hales and pulls me . . .

OTHELLO   Now he tells how she plucked him to my chamber. O, I see that nose of yours, but not the dog I shall throw it to!

Bianca enters. She is clutching the handkerchief.

BIANCA   (*flourishing it*) This is some minx's token, and I must take out the work? There!

OTHELLO   By heaven, that should be my handkerchief!

Bianca throws the handkerchief at Cassio, and stalks away indignantly.

IAGO   After her, after her!

CASSIO   Faith, I must. She'll rail in the streets else. (*He follows.*)

OTHELLO   (*emerging from concealment*) How shall I murder him, Iago? I would have him nine years a-killing. A fine woman, a fair woman, a sweet woman!

IAGO	Nay, you must forget that.
OTHELLO	No, my heart is turned to stone. I strike it, and it hurts my hand. O, the world hath not a sweeter creature! O Iago, the pity of it, Iago!
IAGO	If you are so fond over her iniquity –
OTHELLO	Get me some poison, Iago, this night. This night, Iago!
IAGO	Do it not with poison; strangle her in her bed, even the bed she hath contaminated. And for Cassio, let me be his undertaker.
OTHELLO	Good, good! The justice of it pleases.

A trumpet sounds. The two men stare. At the harbour, Lodovico, the ambassador from the duke, disembarks and is greeted by Desdemona. Othello, accompanied by Iago, appears and Lodovico gives him a letter.

LODOVICO	(*to Othello*) The Duke and Senators of Venice greet you. (*To Desdemona*) How does Lieutenant Cassio?

Frowning, Othello moves away, reading.

DESDEMONA	Cousin, there's fallen between him and my lord an unkind breach; I would do much to atone them, for the love I bear to Cassio.

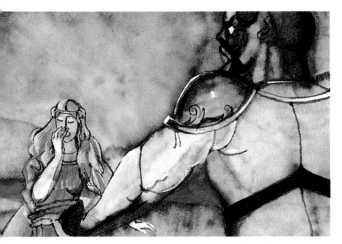 

OTHELLO	Devil! (*He strikes her.*)
DESDEMONA	(*weeping*) I have not deserved this.
LODOVICO	(*comforting her*) Maybe the letter moved him for as I think they do command him home. (*To Othello*) My lord, make her amends; she weeps.
OTHELLO	O devil, devil! Out of my sight! (*Bewildered, Desdemona departs.*) Sir, I obey the mandate, and will return to Venice.

Othello rushes away.

LODOVICO	(*to Iago*) Is this the noble Moor whom our full senate call all-in-all sufficient? Are his wits safe?
IAGO	Alas, alas! It is not honesty in me to speak what I have seen and known. Do but go after and mark how he continues . . .

Desdemona's bedchamber. She is seated with Emilia. Othello enters.

OTHELLO   Let me see your eyes; look in my face. (*He dismisses Emilia with a wave of his hand. She goes.*) What art thou?

DESDEMONA   Your wife, my lord, your true and loyal wife.

OTHELLO   Are you not a strumpet?

DESDEMONA   No, as I shall be saved!

OTHELLO   I cry you mercy. I took you for that cunning whore of Venice that married with Othello.

He rushes from the room. Emilia returns with Iago, to comfort Desdemona.

EMILA   How do you, madam?

IAGO   What is the matter, my lady?

EMILIA   He called her whore.

DESDEMONA   O good Iago, what shall I do to win my lord again?

IAGO   'Tis but his humour, the business of the state does him offence, and he does chide with you. Weep not, all things shall be well. (*He leaves.*)

DESDEMONA   (*as Emilia unpins her hair and begins to brush it.*) How foolish are our minds! My mother had a maid called Barbary, and he she loved proved mad, and did forsake her; she had a song of 'willow', and she died singing it; that song tonight will not go from my mind.

EMILIA   Come, come, you talk.

DESDEMONA   (*singing*)
    The poor soul sat sighing by a sycamore tree,
    Sing all a green willow;
    Her hand on her bosom, her head on her knee,
    Sing willow, willow, willow,
    Sing willow, willow, willow,
    Must be my garland . . .

As she sings, Othello, by an open window, hears the song faintly. He frowns and stares down into the dark town below. There, Iago waits in the street near the palace for Roderigo.

IAGO   If thou hast purpose, courage, valour, then this night show it.

RODERIGO   I have no great devotion to the deed . . .

IAGO   Fear nothing, I'll be at thy elbow.

Cassio bids farewell to Bianca and comes out into the street.

IAGO   (*to himself*) Whether he kill Cassio, or Cassio him, or each do kill the other, every way makes my game.

A scuffle of shadows. Roderigo attacks Cassio. He falls and is himself wounded. He crawls away. Iago darts forward and stabs Cassio from behind, and then vanishes into concealment. There are shouts and cries.

CASSIO   Help, ho! Murder, murder!

Othello, still by the window, hears the shout.

OTHELLO   The voice of Cassio: Iago keeps his word. O brave Iago, thou hast such noble sense of thy friend's wrong! Thou teachest me . . . (*He leaves the room.*)

The street is alive with torches and anxious faces, surrounding the wounded Cassio. Among them are Lodovico and Iago.

IAGO   O my lieutenant! What villains have done this?

A voice calls from the shadows.

RODERIGO'S VOICE   O, help me here!

CASSIO   That's one of them!

IAGO   (*finding Roderigo*) O murderous slave! (*He stabs him.*)

RODERIGO   O damned Iago! O inhuman dog! (*He dies.*)

IAGO   (*staring up towards the castle from which Othello has looked down*) This is the night that either makes me, or fordoes me quite.

In her bedchamber, Desdemona lies on her bed. She closes her eyes. Quietly, Othello enters. He gazes first at the sleeping Desdemona, then at the candle beside her.

OTHELLO Put out the light, and then put out the light: if I quench thee, thou flaming minister, I can again thy former light restore, should I repent me; but once put out thy light – (*He frowns, then bends to kiss her.*)

DESDEMONA Othello?

OTHELLO Ay, Desdemona.

DESDEMONA Will you come to bed, my lord?

OTHELLO Have you prayed tonight, Desdemona?

DESDEMONA Ay, my lord.

OTHELLO If you bethink yourself of any crime unreconciled as yet to heaven and grace, solicit for it straight. I would not kill thy unprepared spirit.

DESDEMONA Then heaven have mercy on me!

OTHELLO The handkerchief which I so loved, and gave thee, thou gavest to Cassio.

DESDEMONA I never gave it him, send for him hither –

OTHELLO	He has confessed.
DESDEMONA	What, my lord?
OTHELLO	That he hath . . . used thee.
DESDEMONA	He will not say so!
OTHELLO	No, his mouth is stopped.
DESDEMONA	Alas, he is betrayed, and I undone!

Othello seizes a pillow.

OTHELLO	Down, strumpet!
DESDEMONA	Kill me tomorrow, let me live tonight!
OTHELLO	Nay, an' you strive –
DESDEMONA	But half an hour!
OTHELLO	It is too late!

He presses the pillow down on her face to suffocate her. There is a knocking on the door.

EMILIA'S VOICE	My lord, my lord!
OTHELLO	'Tis Emilia! If she come in, she'll sure speak to my wife – my wife, my wife! What wife? I have no wife! O insupportable –
EMILIA	I do beseech you that I may speak with you!
OTHELLO	O, come in, Emilia.

He draws the bed curtains and goes to unlock the door. Emilia enters and moves towards the bed.

DESDEMONA	(*faintly*) O falsely, falsely murdered!
EMILIA	(*rushing to draw back the bed curtains*) O, lady, speak again! Who hath done this deed?
DESDEMONA	Nobody; I myself. Commend me to my kind lord. O farewell. (*She dies.*)
OTHELLO	She's like a liar gone to burning hell: 'twas I that killed her!
EMILIA	O, the more angel she, and you the blacker devil!
OTHELLO	She was as false as water!
EMILIA	Thou as rash as fire to say that she was false!
OTHELLO	Cassio did top her: ask thy husband else.
EMILIA	My husband?
OTHELLO	Ay, 'twas he that told me first –
EMILIA	My husband?
OTHELLO	I say thy husband. My friend, thy husband, honest, honest Iago.
EMILIA	If he say so, may his pernicious soul rot half a grain a day! Help, help, ho! help! The Moor hath killed my mistress!

Montano and Iago burst into the room. They see the murdered Desdemona.

MONTANO   O monstrous act!

OTHELLO   'Tis pitiful; but yet Iago knows that she with Cassio hath the act of shame a thousand times committed. Cassio confessed it, and she did gratify his amorous works with the recognisance and pledge of love which I first gave her. I saw it in his hand: it was a handkerchief.

EMILIA   'Twill out, it will out! O thou dull Moor, that handkerchief thou speakest on I found by fortune and did give my husband. He begged of me to steal it –

IAGO   Filth, thou liest!

He stabs Emilia from behind, and escapes. Emilia falls, dying, on the bed. Montano pursues Iago.

EMILIA   (*dying*) Moor, she was chaste; she loved thee, cruel Moor.

She dies. Othello gazes down upon the dead Desdemona. With horror he begins to understand the full extent of Iago's treachery.

OTHELLO   O ill-starred wench! Pale as thy smock! When we shall meet at compt this look of thine will hurl my soul from heaven and fiends will snatch at it. Cold, cold my girl, even like thy chastity.

Montano, Lodovico, and the wounded Cassio enter with Iago, guarded. Othello stares at Iago, and approaches him.

OTHELLO   If that thou be'st a devil, I cannot kill thee. (*He wounds him with his sword. At once, soldiers disarm him.*)

IAGO   I bleed, sir, but not killed.

LODOVICO   This wretch hath part confessed his villainy.

CASSIO   Dear general, I did never give you cause.

OTHELLO   I do believe it, and I ask your pardon. Will you, I pray, demand that demi-devil why he hath thus ensnared my soul and body?

IAGO   Demand me nothing; what you know, you know. From this time forth I never will speak word.

LODOVICO   (*to Othello*) You must forsake this room and go with us –

OTHELLO   Soft you, a word or two. I have done the state some service and they know't. I pray you in your letters when you shall these unlucky deeds relate, speak of them as they are; nothing extenuate nor set down aught in malice. Then must you speak of one that loved not wisely, but too well. Set you down this; and say besides that in Aleppo once where a malignant and a turbaned Turk beat a Venetian and traduced the state, I took by the throat the circumcised dog and smote him thus! (*He stabs himself and falls beside Desdemona.*) I kissed thee ere I killed thee: no way but this, killing myself, to die upon a kiss.

The curtain falls.

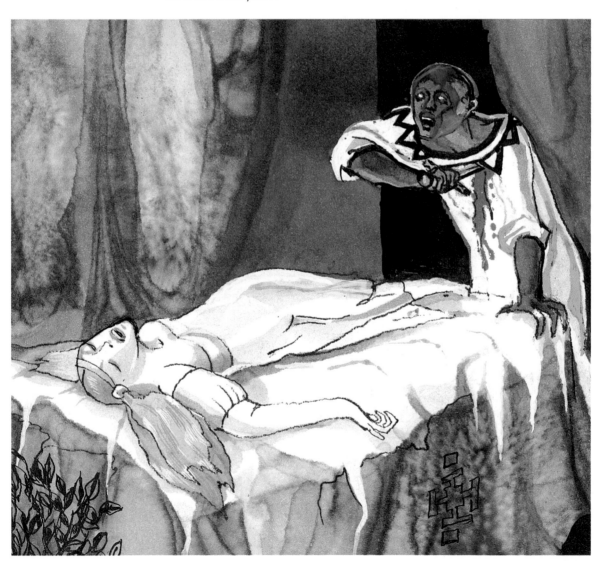

THE WINTER'S TALE

To my mind, of all Shakespeare's plays, *The Winter's Tale* is the most moving and the most magical. It is the story of King Leontes of Sicily, who, in a fit of mad jealousy, brings about the death of his beloved little son and his gracious queen, and causes his baby daughter to be carried away to some wild and savage place, and there left to the mercy of the elements. It is the story of that little daughter and what becomes of her; and of the old shepherd who finds her and brings her up as his own, not knowing she is a princess until —

The first part of the play is all terror and darkness; the second, all laughter and light. "Thou met'st with things dying," says the old shepherd to his son who has come to tell him of a man being eaten by a bear; "and I with things new-born," he says, and shows him the babe.

LEON GARFIELD

On a terrible day, a sudden madness strikes down Leontes, the king of Sicilia. In the twinkling of an eye, it turns him against those he loves best: Hermione, his queen, and Polixenes, king of Bohemia, his childhood friend and guest. He becomes convinced they are lovers and Polixenes the father of Hermione's unborn child.

The curtain rises on the palace of Leontes. It is winter. Polixenes and Hermione walk together. Leontes watches from a little distance, his arm about the shoulders of Mamillius, his little son.

LEONTES   Too hot, too hot! To mingle friendship far is mingling bloods. I have tremor cordis on me; my heart dances, but not for joy – not joy. Go play, boy, play. Thy mother plays, and I play too, but so disgrac'd a part. How now, boy? What! Hast smutched thy nose? They say it is a copy out of mine. Come, captain, we must be neat. (*He wipes his nose.*)

MAMILLIUS   I am like you, they say.

LEONTES   Why, that's some comfort. Go play, Mamillius.

Mamillius leaves.

LEONTES   What! Camillo there?

CAMILLO   Ay, my good lord.

LEONTES   Ha' not you seen, Camillo – but that's past doubt – that my wife is slippery?

CAMILLO   You never spoke what did become you less than this!

LEONTES   Is whispering nothing? Is leaning cheek to cheek? Kissing with inside lip? Is this nothing?

CAMILLO   Good my lord, be cur'd of this diseas'd opinion, and betimes, for 'tis most dangerous.

LEONTES   Say it be, 'tis true.

CAMILLO   No, no, my lord!

LEONTES   It is: you lie. Might'st bespice a cup to give mine enemy a lasting wink?

Leontes departs.

CAMILLO   What case stand I in? I must be the poisoner of good Polixenes.

Polixenes enters.

POLIXENES   The king hath on him such a countenance as he had lost some province. What is breeding that changes thus his manners?

CAMILLO   Sir, I will tell you – I am appointed him to murder you.

POLIXENES   By whom, Camillo?

CAMILLO   By the king.

POLIXENES   For what?

CAMILLO   He thinks, nay, with all confidence he swears, that you have touch'd his queen forbiddenly.

POLIXENES   O then, my best blood turn to an infected jelly! How should this grow?

CAMILLO   I know not; but I am sure 'tis safer to avoid what's grown than question how 'tis born. For myself, I'll put my fortunes to your service, which are here by this discovery lost.

POLIXENES   I do believe thee: I saw his heart in's face. Give me thy hand. My ships are ready.

In the queen's apartment, Hermione is with her ladies who are playing with little Mamillius.

HERMIONE   Come, sir, pray you sit by us, and tell's a tale.

MAMILLIUS   Merry, or sad, shall't be?

HERMIONE   As merry as you will.

MAMILLIUS   A sad tale's best for winter. I have one of sprites and goblins.

HERMIONE   Sit down, and do your best to fright me with your sprites.

MAMILLIUS   There was a man – dwelt by a churchyard . . .

Leontes and lords enter.

LEONTES   Bear the boy hence, he shall not come about her.

HERMIONE   What is this? Sport?

LEONTES   Away with him! And let her sport herself with that she's big with, for 'tis Polixenes has made thee swell thus. She's an adultress! (*The child is removed.*)

HERMIONE   Should a villain say so, the most replenish'd villain in the world, he were as much more villain: you, my lord, do but mistake.

LEONTES   You have mistook, my lady, Polixenes for Leontes. Away with her, to prison!

HERMIONE   Adieu, my lord, I never wish'd to see you sorry; now I trust I shall.

The queen departs under guard. Her ladies are in tears but she does not cry and gestures to them to be brave as she passes. Antigonus, an old nobleman, speaks up for her.

ANTIGONUS   I dare my life lay down that the queen is spotless.

LEONTES   Cease, no more. You smell this business with a sense as cold as is a dead man's nose; but I do see't and feel't. I have dispatch'd to sacred Delphos, to Apollo's temple. Though I am satisfied, yet shall the Oracle give rest to th'minds of others – such as he. (*He points to Antigonus.*)

Mamillius has fallen sick and a servant brings news of the child's condition to Leontes.

LEONTES	How does the boy?
SERVANT	He took good rest tonight; 'tis hop'd his sickness is discharg'd.
LEONTES	Go, see how he fares.

Hermione, in prison, has given birth to an infant girl. Her good friend, Paulina, wife of Antigonus, decides to take the baby to Leontes in the hope of curing him of his madness. But when she attempts to gain audience with Leontes, he is outraged.

LEONTES	Away with that audacious lady! Antigonus, I charg'd thee that she should not come about me. Canst not rule her?
ANTIGONUS	Hang all the husbands that cannot do that feat, you'll leave yourself hardly one subject.
PAULINA	Good my liege, I come from your good queen.
LEONTES	Good queen?
PAULINA	The good queen – for she is good – hath brought you forth a daughter, here 'tis.

LEONTES   A mankind witch! Hence with her, out o' door! Give her the bastard, thou dotard! Tak't up, I say: give it to thy crone!

Antigonus stands frozen.

LEONTES   He dreads his wife. This brat is none of mine.

PAULINA   It is yours: and so like you, 'tis the worse.

LEONTES   I'll have thee burnt!

PAULINA   I care not.

LEONTES   Out of the chamber with her!

PAULINA   I'll be gone. Look to your babe, my lord, 'tis yours.

She departs, leaving the child to its father's mercy.

LEONTES   Thou, traitor, hast set on thy wife to this. My child? Away with't! Go, take it to the fire.

LORD   Beseech your highness, on our knees we beg that you do change this purpose, which, being so horrible, so bloody, must lead on to some foul issue.

They kneel.

LEONTES   Be it: let it live. What will you adventure to save this brat's life?

ANTIGONUS   Any thing, my lord.

LEONTES   Mark, and perform it. We enjoin thee that thou carry this female bastard hence, and that thou bear it to some remote and desert place, quite out of our dominions; and that there thou leave it to its own protection: take it up.

ANTIGONUS   Come on, poor babe: some powerful spirit instruct the kites and ravens to be thy nurses.

Antigonus takes up the babe and hastens away.

SERVANT   Please your highness, posts from those you sent to the Oracle are come.

LEONTES   Prepare you, my lords, summon a session that we may arraign our most disloyal lady.

In the place of justice, Hermione stands before her accuser.

JUDGE   Hermione, queen to the worthy Leontes, king of Sicilia, thou art here accused and arraigned of high treason, in committing adultery with Polixenes, king of Bohemia.

HERMIONE   You, my lord, best know my past life hath been as continent, as chaste, as true, as I am now unhappy. Your honours, I do refer me to the Oracle: Apollo be my judge!

LORD   This your request is altogether just.

            The officers go to fetch the messengers.

HERMIONE   The Emperor of Russia was my father. O that he were alive,
            and here beholding his daughter's trial! That he did but see the
            flatness of my misery, yet with eyes of pity, not revenge.

            The officers return with the two messengers.

LEONTES   Break up the seals and read.

JUDGE   (*reading*) Hermione is chaste; Polixenes blameless; Camillo a
            true subject; Leontes a jealous tyrant; his innocent babe truly
            begotten; and the king shall live without an heir, if that which
            is lost be not found.

LORDS   Now blessed be the great Apollo.

LEONTES   There is no truth at all in the Oracle!

There is a clap of thunder. A servant rushes in.

LEONTES The sessions shall proceed: this is mere falsehood.

SERVANT My lord the king! Your son is gone!

LEONTES How? Gone?

SERVANT Is dead.

Leontes stares in horror at what his madness has brought about.

LEONTES Apollo's angry, and the heavens themselves do strike at my injustice!

Hermione swoons. She is carried away by her ladies with Paulina in tearful attendance.

PAULINA This news is mortal to the queen. Look down and see what death is doing.

LEONTES Take her hence. Beseech you, tenderly apply to her some remedies for life. I'll reconcile me to Polixenes, new woo my queen, recall the good Camillo. How his piety does my deeds make the blacker!

Paulina returns.

PAULINA   The queen! The sweet'st, dear'st creature's dead! O thou tyrant! Betake thee to nothing but despair.

LEONTES   Go on, go on: I have deserv'd all tongues to talk their bitt'rest. Prithee bring me to the dead bodies of my queen and son; one grave shall be for both: upon them shall the causes of their deaths appear, unto our shame perpetual.

Antigonus, obeying his master's harsh command, takes the babe and sets sail from Sicilia. On board ship, Antigonus has a strange vision in which Hermione appears before him. Such is the nature of the vision that Antigonus is convinced of Hermione's guilt.

HERMIONE   Good Antigonus, since fate hath made thy person for the thrower-out of my poor babe, places remote enough are in Bohemia, there weep, and leave it crying; and, for the babe is counted lost forever, Perdita, I prithee call it.

Antigonus, having landed on the rocky sea coast of Bohemia in the midst of a terrible storm, leaves the child to its fate.

ANTIGONUS   Blossom, speed thee well. There lie, and there thy character.

He places a box and bundle of possessions beside the baby.

ANTIGONUS Farewell, the day frowns more and more: thou'rt like to have a lullaby too rough. (*A bear appears.*) I am gone forever! (*Exit, pursued by a bear.*)

The storm increases in fury and overwhelms the waiting ship. Meanwhile, a shepherd searching for lost sheep, comes upon the babe.

SHEPHERD What have we here? Mercy on's, a barne? I'll take it up for pity: yet I'll tarry till my son come. Ahoa!

An answering shout. Enter the shepherd's son.

SON I have seen two such sights, by sea and land!

SHEPHERD Why boy, how is it?

In answer to the shepherd's question, the son tells how he saw all the sailors drowned and Antigonus eaten by the bear.

SHEPHERD   Now bless thyself: thou met'st with things dying, I with things new born. Here's a sight for thee: look thee, a bearing-cloth for a squire's child. Look thee here, take up, boy, open it. What's within, boy?

His son opens the box and finds Hermione's jewels.

SON   You're a made old man! Gold! All gold!

SHEPHERD   This is fairy gold, and 'twill prove so. 'Tis a lucky day, boy, and we'll do good deeds on't.

The sky lightens and across the landscape of Bohemia a strange spectre strides: a pale figure bearing an hourglass. It is Time.

TIME   In the name of Time, I slide over sixteen years. In fair Bohemia, a son of the king's which Florizel I now name to you. And Perdita now grown in grace, a shepherd's daughter.

In the royal palace, Polixenes and Camillo stand together, gazing out of the window. It is high summer.

POLIXENES   Say to me, when sawest thou the Prince Florizel, my son?

CAMILLO   Sir, it is three days since I saw the prince.

POLIXENES   I have this intelligence, that he is seldom from the house of a most homely shepherd: a man, they say, that from very nothing, is grown into an unspeakable estate.

CAMILLO   I have heard, sir, of such a man, who hath a daughter of most rare note.

POLIXENES   Thou shalt accompany us to the place.

CAMILLO   I obey your command.

POLIXENES   My best Camillo! We must disguise ourselves.

On a country road, a lively figure appears. It is Autolycus, a cheerful pilferer of everything that has not been nailed down.

AUTOLYCUS   (*singing*) When daffodils begin to peer,
              With heigh the doxy over the dale,
              Why then comes in the sweet o' the year.
              For the red blood reigns in the winter's pale.

My father named me Autolycus, who was likewise a snapper-up of unconsidered trifles. (*He sees the shepherd's son approaching.*) A prize, a prize!

SON   Let me see, what am I to buy for our sheep-shearing feast? Three pound of sugar, five pound of currants, rice: what will this sister of mine do with rice? But my father hath made her Mistress of the Feast —

Autolycus flings himself in the son's path, wailing and moaning.

AUTOLYCUS   O help me, help me! I am robbed, sir, and beaten.

SON   Lend me thy hand, I'll help thee.

AUTOLYCUS   O good sir, tenderly, oh!

As the son helps Autolycus to his feet, his pocket is skilfully picked.

SON   How now? Canst stand? Dost lack any money? I have a little money for thee.

AUTOLYCUS   No, good sweet sir! Offer me no money, I pray you; that kills my heart.

SON   Then fare thee well, I must go buy spices for our sheep-shearing.

The son departs.

AUTOLYCUS   (*examining his booty*) Prosper you, sweet sir. I'll be with you at your sheep-shearing too. (*He sets off along the road, singing.*)

> Jog on, jog on, the footpath way,
> And merrily hent the stile-a:
> A merry heart goes all the day.
> Your sad tires in a mile-a.

Before the shepherd's cottage, everything is in readiness for the sheep-shearing. There is music and dancing and Perdita, attired as Queen of the Feast, speaks to Florizel who is dressed as a very grand shepherd.
She moves away from Florizel and gives flowers and herbs to Polixenes and Camillo who are strangers at the feast.

PERDITA   Reverend sirs, for you, there's rosemary and rue; grace and remembrance be to you both, and welcome to our sheep-shearing.

Florizel returns to her side.

FLORIZEL   Come, our dance I pray, your hand, my Perdita.

He leads her off and they join the dance.

POLIXENES   This is the prettiest low-born lass, that ever ran on greensward.

CAMILLO   Good sooth, she is the queen of curds and cream!

POLIXENES   Pray good shepherd, what fair swain is this, which dances with your daughter?

SHEPHERD   They call him Doricles. He says he loves my daughter: I think so too. I think there is not half a kiss to choose who loves another best. (*Autolycus enters, singing.*)

AUTOLYCUS   Will you buy any tape,
                     Or lace for your cape,
                     My dainty duck, my dear-a?
                     Any silk, any thread,
                     Any toys for your head . . .
                     Of the new'st, and fin'st, wear-a?

The dancers eagerly stream after him. Perdita and Florizel are left. Polixenes beckons them near.

POLIXENES	Sooth, when I was young, and handed love, as you do, I was wont to load my she with knacks; I would have ransack'd the pedlar's silken treasury –
FLORIZEL	(*with dramatic sincerity*) Old sir, I know she prizes not such trifles as these are. The gifts she looks from me, are pack'd and lock'd up in my heart, which I have given already, but not delivered.
SHEPHERD	Take hands, a bargain; and friends unknown, you shall bear witness to't: I give my daughter to him, and will make her portion equal his. Come, your hand: and daughter, yours.
POLIXENES	Soft, swain, awhile, beseech you. Have you a father?
FLORIZEL	I have: but what of him?
POLIXENES	Knows he of this?
FLORIZEL	He neither does, nor shall.
POLIXENES	By my white beard, you offer him a wrong something unfilial. Let him know't.

FLORIZEL   He shall not: mark our contract.

POLIXENES   (*revealing himself*) Mark your divorce, young sir, whom son I
dare not call: thou art too base to be acknowledged; thou a
sceptre's heir that thus affects a sheep-hook! Thou, old traitor,
I am sorry, that by hanging thee, I can but shorten thy life one
week. And thou, if ever henceforth thou hoop his body more
with thy embraces, I will devise a death, as cruel for thee as
thou art tender to't.

He storms away, leaving all aghast.

PERDITA   I was not much afeared: for once, or twice I was about to
speak, and tell him plainly, the self-same sun that shines upon
his court hides not his visage from our cottage, but looks on
alike. (*To Florizel*) Will't please you, sir, be gone?

SHEPHERD   O sir, you have undone a man of fourscore three. (*To Perdita*)
O cursed wretch, thou knew'st this was the prince! Undone,
undone! If I might die within this hour, I have lived to die when
I desire.

The old shepherd leaves.

FLORIZEL   (*to Camillo and Perdita*) Why look you so upon me? I am sorry, not afear'd: delay'd, but nothing alter'd: what I was, I am —

CAMILLO   Gracious my lord —

FLORIZEL   Camillo, not for Bohemia will I break my oath to this fair belov'd. This you may know, and so deliver, I am put to sea with her whom here I cannot hold on shore. I have a vessel rides fast by.

CAMILLO   This is desperate sir. Have you thought on a place whereto you'll go?

FLORIZEL   Not any yet.

CAMILLO   Then list to me. Make for Sicilia and there present yourself and your fair princess 'fore Leontes. (*Autolycus walks by.*) We'll make an instrument of this. How now, good fellow?

AUTOLYCUS   I am a poor fellow, sir.

CAMILLO   Why, be so still. Yet for the outside of thy poverty we must make an exchange: therefore discase thee instantly and change garments with this gentleman. There's some boot. (*Gives him money.*) What I do next shall be to tell the king of this escape to force him after.

*The terrified shepherd and his son are on their way to the
palace with the box and bundle of possessions that they found
with the infant Perdita.*

SON — There is no other way but to tell the king she's a changeling,
and none of your flesh and blood.

SHEPHERD — I will tell the king all, every word, yea, and his son's pranks
too. There is that in this fardel will make him scratch his beard.
(*He taps the bundle.*)

Autolycus enters. He has overheard the last.

AUTOLYCUS — How now, rustics, whither are you bound?

SHEPHERD — To the palace, and it like your worship.

AUTOLYCUS — What's in the fardel? Wherefore that box?

SHEPHERD — Sir, there lies such secrets in this fardel and box which none
must know but the king.

AUTOLYCUS — Age, thou hast lost thy labour. The king is not at the palace. He
is gone aboard a new ship. I'll bring you where he is.

SON He seems to be of great authority. Close with him, give him gold.

SHEPHERD An't please you sir, to undertake the business for us, here is that gold I have.

AUTOLYCUS Walk before, toward the sea-side. (*They walk on.*) If I had a mind to be honest, I see Fortune would not suffer me: she drops booties in my mouth. To the prince will I present them, there may be matter in it.

In Sicilia, Leontes still mourns the loss of his Hermione as does Paulina of her Antigonus. His lords try to persuade him to take another wife.

LORD Sir, you have done enough, and have perform'd a saint-like sorrow.

PAULINA   You are one of those would have him wed again. There is none
           worthy, respecting her that's gone. Besides, has not the divine
           Apollo said that King Leontes shall not have an heir till his lost
           child be found?

LEONTES   My true Paulina, we shall not marry till thou bid'st us.

PAULINA   That shall be when your first queen's again in breath: never till
           then. (*As she speaks, a servant enters.*)

SERVANT   One that gives out himself Prince Florizel, son of Polixenes,
           with his princess – she the fairest I have yet beheld – desires
           access to your high presence.

LEONTES   He comes not like to his father's greatness. Bring them to our
           embracement. Still, 'tis strange he thus should steal upon us.

Florizel and Perdita enter.

LEONTES   Were I but twenty-one, your father's image is so hit in you – his very air – that I should call you brother. Welcome hither, as is the spring to th'earth.

A lord enters.

LORD   Please you, great sir, Polixenes greets you from himself by me; desires you to attach his son, who has fled from his father, from his hopes, and with a shepherd's daughter.

LEONTES   Where's Polixenes? Speak.

LORD   Here, in your city. To your court whiles he was hastening, meets he on the way the father of this seeming lady and her brother.

PERDITA   O my poor father!

LEONTES   (*to Florizel*) You are married?

FLORIZEL   We are not, sir, nor are we like to be.

LEONTES   My lord, is this the daughter of a king?

FLORIZEL   She is, when once she is my wife.

LEONTES   That 'once', I see, by your good father's speed, will come on very slowly.

FLORIZEL   Beseech you sir, step forth mine advocate. At your request, my father will grant precious things as trifles.

LEONTES   I will to your father. Come.

In Sicilia, church bells are ringing everywhere. The two kings have met. The old shepherd's box and bundle which contained the secrets of Perdita's birth have been opened. The Oracle has been fulfilled: the king's daughter has been found.

Autolycus and three gentlemen enter. A fourth approaches.

1ST GENTLEMAN   This news, which is so like an old tale: has the king found his heir?

3RD GENTLEMAN   Most true. Did you see the meeting of the two kings?

2ND GENTLEMAN   No.

3RD GENTLEMAN   Then have you lost a sight! Our king being ready to leap out of himself, for joy of his found daughter, cries 'O, thy mother, thy mother!' Then asks Polixenes forgiveness, then embraces his son-in-law, now he thanks the old shepherd.

4TH GENTLEMAN   The princess hearing of her mother's statue – which is in the keeping of Paulina – a piece many years in doing, by that rare Italian master, Julio Romano – thither are they gone.

1ST GENTLEMAN   Let's along.

They depart, leaving Autolycus. The old shepherd and his son approach. They are splendidly dressed.

AUTOLYCUS   Here come those I have done good to against my will. (*He bows to them.*) I humbly beseech you, sir, to pardon me all the faults I have committed.

SHEPHERD   Prithee, son, do: for we must be gentle, now we are gentlemen.

SON   Thou wilt amend thy life?

AUTOLYCUS   Ay, and it like your good worship.

SON   Come, follow us: we'll be thy good masters.

*All are assembled in a chapel in Paulina's house. The statue of
Hermione is hidden behind a curtain.*

LEONTES   O Paulina, we came to see the statue of our queen.

PAULINA   Here it is. (*Draws back the curtain*). Comes it not something
near?

LEONTES   Her natural posture. Chide me, dear stone, that I may say
indeed thou art Hermione. But yet, Paulina, Hermione was not
so much wrinkled, nothing so aged as this seems.

POLIXENES   Oh, not by much.

PAULINA   So much the more our carver's excellence, which lets go by
some sixteen years, and makes her as she liv'd now.

LEONTES   As now she might have done. Oh royal piece, there's magic in
thy majesty.

PERDITA   (*kneeling*) Lady, dear queen, that ended when I but began, give me that hand of yours, to kiss.

PAULINA   O patience: the statue is but newly fix'd; the colour's not dry.

LEONTES   Let no man mock me, for I will kiss her.

PAULINA   Good my lord, forbear; the ruddiness upon her lip is wet: you'll mar it if you kiss it. Shall I draw the curtain?

LEONTES   No: not these twenty years.

PERDITA   So long could I stand by, a looker-on.

PAULINA   If you can behold it, I'll make the statue move indeed; descend, and take you by the hand. It is requir'd you do awake your faith. Music, awake her; strike; 'tis time; descend; be stone no more; approach.

The statue descends. It is Hermione herself. She is alive and holds out her hands to Leontes.

PAULINA   When she was young, you woo'd her: now, in age, is she become the suitor?

LEONTES   (*taking Hermione's hand*) Oh she's warm! If this be magic, let it be an art lawful as eating.

Hermione embraces Leontes – silence descends as she hangs on his neck.

CAMILLO   If she pertain to life, let her speak too.

PAULINA   Mark a little while. (*To Perdita*) Please you to interpose, fair madam, kneel, and pray your mother's blessing; turn, good lady, our Perdita is found.

HERMIONE   (*crying, her tears falling as a heavenly blessing on her daughter*) You Gods look down, and from your sacred vials pour your graces upon my daughter's head! Tell me, mine own, where hast thou been preserv'd? where liv'd?

PAULINA   There's time enough for that. Go together, you precious winners all. I, an old turtle, will wing me to some wither'd bough, and there my mate, that's never to be found again, lament, till I am lost.

LEONTES   O peace, Paulina! Thou should'st a husband take by my consent, as I by thine a wife. Come, Camillo, and take her by the hand. Good Paulina, lead us from hence, where we may leisurely each one demand, and answer to his part perform'd in this wide gap of time, since first we were dissever'd.

The curtain falls.